THE CREW

CHAFFCUTTER

The Author, Tom Peppitt
as a Merchant Navy Junior Apprentice,
learning the hard way!

© Tom Peppitt, 2000

Typeset in 11/13pt Times

Published by
Chaffcutter Books
in association with the Society for Sailing Barge Research

ISBN 0 9532422 2 6

Chaffcutter Books is the publishing division of
Isla Giatt Limited, 25 Buntingford Road, Puckeridge, Ware, Hertfordshire SG11 1RT, England

Printed and bound in Great Britain by
The Lavenham Press Limited, Water Street, Lavenham, Suffolk CO10 9RN, England

THE CREW

Tom Peppitt

**A Portrait of Merchant Seamen
at the End of the Tramp Steamer Era**

Chaffcutter Books

Contents

To Dick Fraser, Late Chief Officer of T.S. Mercury;
Ave et Atque, - sleep well my old friend and mentor.

Introduction

The Author has done a remarkable job in recording in this series of vignettes, the characters and backgrounds of the men who made up the crews of the tramp ships of the 1940s and 50s - and of the life they had to live. He is, of course, writing of history and it is very important that this piece of our maritime heritage has been written down for future generations to understand and marvel at.

I am particularly interested in these accounts for I was part of a company owning ships of the type and age he describes. Not only do I recognise very much of what he has recorded, but have also learnt much more from it which I did not realise at the time.

But primarily it is history, for while he is of course right when he says that the ships he sailed in were already out of date, they were also very much on the way out even then, and by the 1950s were unsaleable except to fairly disreputable owners. My own company had three coal burners left in the fleet at the end of the war, one built in 1929 (on which the Author sailed as a Junior Apprentice), and two built on very similar lines by the same Scottish yard in 1939/40. We also managed four war built ships for the Government which we bought in at the end of hostilities and, triggered by the example of one of them, a Liberty ship, proceeded to convert all except the oldest to oil firing, trading with them until it became possible to build new tonnage in the 1950s.

Life was clearly tough in the coal burners, with twelve fireman trimmers to deal, by hand, with typically thirty-two tons of coal a day, and on one of our worst voyages, with bad coal loaded at Vancouver, forty-eight tons a day. And when I came back from six years in the Army I was ashamed of the living conditions we were providing at sea, and we modified, to an extent, all the ships - again except the oldest.

One of the aspects which the Author brings out very clearly is the difficulty in communication between 'them and us', ship and shore. Subsequent shore based academic studies defined the problem as one of a sense of alienation in seagoing staff, not understood by those ashore, but if true (as I think it probably was) it was far from clear what could be done about it. There was no agreement on this between all the parties when I retired in 1986, but these vignettes seem to suggest that any reduction in the differences between officers and ratings at sea, which was one of the suggestions made, would have achieved precious little.

But maybe it does not matter any more because, sadly, there is very little British shipping left - and very few British seafarers. And the sort of companies which owned the ships about which the Author writes have disappeared as mine did in the 1980s.

So it is history, but history the better for being recorded.

Sir Frederic Bolton
Chipping Norton
Oxfordshire

Preface

This is the true story of a closed community of seamen, the world of the tramp ship in the closing years of the coal burning era. They were ordinary men forced to live an almost monastic existence for the greater part of their lives, and this of itself was directly responsible for many of their wilder moments. No excuse is offered for the politically incorrect male chauvinism of many of the characters, or for my style in writing about them. The same is true of any seemingly racist remarks, it was a time when there was less colour consciousness than now, and virtually none at sea. I paid more notice to the colour of the going ashore clothes of my friends and shipmates than I did to the colour of their skins. It is their story and if their ways or mine are no longer acceptable to current morals then I apologise for them, but cannot now change mid twentieth century life styles while still keeping faith with my erstwhile shipmates.

This is not an adventure story, but a portrait of the men themselves, as they really were; the cockney Third Mate who played the bagpipes, the Cook in red carpet slippers, the Chief Engineer who painted nudes, the Marine Super with his grey trilby. These and many others have their entrances and sometimes their exits as well. It is a story told against the backdrop of their workaday lives; the chaos of a ship's galley in a mid-winter gale, stowing anchor cable by hand, chipping, scraping and painting in the tropics, the glow of the stokehold furnaces, the loneliness of the graveyard watch. These reflect the skills of the mid-twentieth century merchant seaman, at a first glance so very different from those of the sailing era.

It follows them, not only around the oceans and sea ports of the world, but also backwards to their origins; Sparks in a Gloucester parsonage, Warren Fitzroy from the Bahamas, Old Jan from a Stornaway croft, the Polish aristocrat, the National Service Corporal. All at some time made the tramp ship their home. Some stayed at sea, but many went their separate ways; Abdul shot dead as a rebel, Pete back to the Royal Navy still dreaming of becoming a fisherman, John Bateman tending barges on a Thamesside gravel pit, Jack and Wally lost at sea many years past, Max back on shore because seafaring was not a nautical enough profession. These and all the others were at some time the author's shipmates, most have now passed on, this is their book.

Tom Peppitt
Kingston
Isle of Wight

Chapter 1

**S.S. Rose Bay,
Their Home**

If in these portraits there is either a hero or a villain, the role must be filled by the ship herself. Several thousand tons of steel and wood cannot really have a personality of its own, but the same ship can over the years be happy and unhappy by turns, depending on the crew and the voyage. For example the *Rose Bay* was a happy ship on the Mediterranean iron ore run, a very dirty trade, but one which allowed her crew to be home at least one week in six. On her next trip, to the Far East, she was out of home waters for over twelve months and on that voyage she could hardly be classed as happy; so perhaps even sailors like to get home occasionally at weekends.

Designed to carry as much cargo as possible - ten thousand tons deadweight - she had none of the streamlined grace of a clipper ship. Nor, because of her sturdy triple cylinder reciprocating engine, did she need a lofty tracery of masts and spars. Her rigging was stark simplicity itself. The two stump masts supporting her derricks were held by twin pairs of shrouds, her topmasts supported by light stays which were only there to carry the main wireless aerial clear of the bridge superstructure and to support her signal halyards. She was a simple cargo carrier, her size emphasised by the comparative smallness of her open bridge and deckhouse, no soaring tower blocks of passenger cabins on A, B and C decks for the Rose Bay. Her true measure was only made plain when the whole of her bulk with its slab sides and flat bottom could be viewed from below in dry dock.

After the second World War the Rose Bay was one of the older coal burning tramps still making deep sea voyages under the Red Ensign, but even then her building date of 1929 belied her design, which was that of almost a decade earlier. Scant regard had been paid to any amenities not strictly laid down by the Board of Trade. In the depression money was so short and so many seamen were unemployed that any luxury for the crew could be cut from her plan. Cabins were small and furnishings spartan; the two apprentices of which I was once one, shared a cabin with a single two foot six inch wide locker, four drawers (two each) and a free floor area measuring but five feet between the bunks and the settee built into the bulkheads. The Third Mate's cabin was even smaller, with only a three foot gangway between bunk and settee, but then he did not have to share. However for all their bleakness at least the midships accommodation did have tongued and grooved panelling on the bulkheads and varnished deal fittings. Down aft the crew had cabins of even smaller dimensions, with unashamed steel sides and green tin lockers. Being officers we had cheap coir mats for carpeting, down aft they had none.

Domestic appointments were just as basic. In our living accommodation amidships we did have a wash hand basin in each cabin, but they were innocent of taps or running water and had only buckets for drains. So all seven of us used our one combined bathroom and toilet every time we washed our hands. Down aft two showers had to serve ten sailors and there were only three showers to serve all sixteen of the firemen. The water we had was not of the best quality either. There was one small seven ton tank solely reserved for drinking and cooking, but the remainder came up from the tanks in the double bottom and out of the bathroom taps any colour from palest beige to deepest orange. That was of course if there was any at all; amidships it was supplied by gravity from a small header tank on the wheelhouse roof which the engineers only filled twice daily. So it might require a trip below to ask the engineer on watch to pump it up before you could shower after a day's work, that is providing he was not busy about some more essential task and providing we were not in the water shortage mode. If the trip between bunkering[1] ports was long the fresh water supply had to be augmented by distilling from salt water and that took steam, which required coal, which was an additional call on expensive bunkers which the company would begrudge. So not infrequently you might either have to use salt water or stay unwashed for quite some time. Nor was it any good trying to phone the engine room to save a trip below; there were no telephones on board. The only direct engine room communication links were two voice pipes, one to the bridge and the other to the Chief Engineer's cabin - and because of engine noise they were virtually useless anyway.

It was this domestic water situation, plus the all pervading dust from our iron ore cargoes that made it abundantly clear to me, fresh from the spit and polish of a training ship, that cleanliness is a comparative, not an absolute term. The oil and grime of the decks could oftimes only be exchanged for the faint, but penetratingly acrid, smell of rusty water, which no amount of talc or after shave could completely eradicate. As a first tripper I came equipped with white shirts but, like everyone else on board, I very soon exchanged them for more practical khaki uniform wear with coloured shirts for going ashore. That way it was just possible to impart an acceptable degree of freshness to one's laundry and in some measure to postpone the inevitable piebald onset of brown rust marks on cotton fabric.

For her motive power the Rose Bay depended on coal, ton upon ton of it, carried in the saddle back bunker forward of the funnel and in the two side pockets

---

1. Bunkering - *Taking on steam coal for the ship's furnaces*

abaft Number Three hatch, and unless we were really topped up with cargo, in Number Three 'tween deck as well. Even with all this coal, a passage from the UK to Australia required at least four intermediate calls for bunkering. We did once make a complete ocean crossing in one hop, from Japan to Vancouver, but that was only because we were in ballast[1] and so could use the shelter deck of Number Three for extra bunkers as well. Carrying so much fuel was not without its minor excitements, for coal can self-ignite at the very low flash point of 77° Fahrenheit. It was not unusual on a long trip to see a thin wisp of smoke curling up from one or other of the fuel stowages. This was not particularly dangerous providing it was detected early enough, but it did mean that the whole crew had to turn to and shovel until the offending portion of the fuel supply was spread around on deck so that it could cool off again. Rarely, if ever, would it be thrown overside for it was far too valuable a commodity to be wasted. These occasions were always something of a break in the normal routine; the Captain would inevitably be there, covered in coal dust, shovelling with the best of them - although as I remember it only for a very short time. He would also bring down the rum bottle to circulate among the crew, a special treat on an otherwise dry ship, for neither the company's regulations nor the size of the provision stores allowed beer to be carried.

The deck and cargo equipment of the Rose Bay were also of a bygone era. On almost every merchant ship then afloat the derrick topping lifts[2] were secured to a 'monkey's face', a triangular steel plate that shackled on to a length of chain fitted to eyebolts on the deck, but the Rose Bay had no truck with such modern devices. Her topping lift wires were cleated directly on to the side of the deck houses. She also had a most archaic rod and chain steering gear, and a rudder equipped with a Dunstos Quadrant Brake. These items were part of the basic merchant ship's steering gear as illustrated in the standard books on seamanship, and the subject of Board of Trade examinations. The only snag was that they had ceased to be fitted on steamships at least a decade earlier so few examinees would ever have seen them in the flesh, let alone sailed with them. Consequently we had a fairly steady stream of earnest seekers after knowledge visiting us from the 'Rolls-Royce' side of the mercantile marine whenever we were in port.

There is an old saying that the last ship is always the best ship, but there was little to recommend the Rose Bay for this honour. She was a back-breaker to work and definitely no home from home. If we were happy on board it was despite of, not because of her and certainly none of us regretted stepping over her gangway for the last time. Inevitably she went the way of many tramps. Sold to flag of convenience owners, running under the name of Granny Suzanne, then Montan and finally Antonio A. Kyrtatas, she grew older and dirtier until eventually she became too uneconomic for even her new owners. Then a final tow to a Hamburg breaker's yard put an end to her career, her steel being rendered down to begin the cycle all over again.

---

1. In ballast - *Without cargo, but with double bottom tanks filled with water*
2. Topping lift - *A cable supporting the upper end of a derrick*

Chapter 2

**Dramatis Personae,
Ship's Company**

The characters in this book are real, I sailed with them all. Their names are changed to avoid embarrassment but if you are an erstwhile shipmate and the character seems familiar then you have probably guessed aright, and I owe you a beer or three. Most are typical crew members from the coal burning tramp ships of the 1940s that became rarities in the 1950s and had virtually disappeared by the 1960s, replaced by larger, faster oil burners.

The ship would be divided into three departments, deck, engine room and catering, with the Captain in overall command as well as being the senior member of the deck department. He was also expected to be on the bridge when entering or leaving port. His immediate subordinate was the 1st Mate who took the 4 to 8 watch as well as being in charge for'ard during docking or departure. He also had responsibility via the deck crew for working the cargo as well as maintenance of deck fittings and painting ship. The 2nd Mate took the 12 to 4 watch at sea and was responsible aft when entering or leaving port. He was responsible for cargo plans and the deck watches in harbour. Navigation and chart correction were also his role. The 3rd Mate took the 8 - 12 watch, shared the deck watch organisation with the 2nd and kept the ship's log of arrivals and departures. He was also in charge of the maintenance of the ship's lifeboats. The Radio Officer's role just covered his domain. The Carpenter, however, was rarely employed in his title role, taking charge of the anchor windlass when entering or leaving port and responsibility for the security of the hatch wedges and battens as well as for fresh water and tank soundings. There were two Apprentices, learning many of their 'skills' under the guidance of the Bosun, who was also responsible for the ten sailors, generally four Ordinary Seamen plus six EDHs[1] or ABs[2], and one of the two Deck Boys. The other Deck Boy worked as the crew's messman. Quite often in the interests of economy the ship would carry only one Deck Boy; nor would it be uncommon for the most skilled deck rating, the Carpenter, to be replaced by the Senior Apprentice at half the former's wage.

1. EDH - *Efficient Deck Hand qualification awarded by the Board of Trade*
2. AB - *Able Bodied Seaman. Qualified seaman with four years service since award of Efficient Deck Hand Certificate*

The Chief Engineer was in overall charge of the engine room. The 2nd Engineer took the 4 to 8 watch at sea and had general responsibility for on board maintenance and for work in the engine room. The 3rd Engineer had the 12 to 4 watch at sea and was the ship's electrician. The 8 to 12 watch fell to the 4th Engineer who also had responsibility for auxiliary machinery in the engine room. The 5th Engineer, when there was one, worked on the maintenance of deck machinery, when the nature of the task demanded. The Donkeyman was the engine room foreman in charge of three Donkey Greasers, one to each watch as Engineer's Assistant. There were usually twelve Firemen Trimmers, four to each watch - one to stoke each of three boilers and one to keep the pockets[1] topped up for the stokers.

The catering needs and associated stores were under the charge of the Chief Steward, as was the ship's first aid chest. The Chief Cook was in charge of the galley. The 2nd Steward looked after the Captain's needs and the 2nd Cook acted as assistant to the Chief Cook and baked the bread. There were two Assistant Stewards, one to serve the Mates, the other for the Engineers. Lastly there was the Galley Boy, slave to the Chief and 2nd Cook, who spent much of his life peeling potatoes.

This then was the ship's company; a wide assortment of roles filled by an even wider assortment of people, all forced to coexist for weeks, months, sometimes even years on end, within the confines of the closed community collectively known as 'the crew'.

1. Pockets - *The fuel hoppers from the bunkers at deck level to the stokehold floor*

Chapter 3

Genesis

John was a conventional suburban London grammar school boy; his parents had ambitions to send him to university and then on into one of the professions. John in turn wanted to be an engine driver, then a fireman, next a cowboy and a sailor at all the usual stages of his schooldays, well before he understood what career with a big 'C' meant. It was at the end of this particular progression that his parents refused him permission to sit for a scholarship to Dartmouth and the Royal Navy. As they were not a naval family, there were no uncles or cousins to prove that this was a right and proper career, so the project was not further discussed. However it was enough to persuade the twelve year old John that the sea should have him. This unwavering determination surfaced again at fourteen when scholarships were offered to the Training Ship Mercury on the Hamble. This time parental reluctance was overcome, possibly because the ship was commanded by the charismatic sportsman C.B. Fry, one of John's father's childhood heroes.

New boys arrived a day before the rest, in order to settle in. Sleeping in a hammock was novel, but surprisingly none of the 'Nozzers'[1] had trouble getting in them. Their first night was memorable for the diminutive figure that appeared sitting like some malignant gnome on the open hatch coaming looking down on the rows of hammocks. It was the Night Officer, who watched over the slumbering ship and its occupants. He wore a blue monkey jacket with two tarnished gold stripes to indicate he was an officer, a white submarine sweater and sea boots to indicate he was a seaman, a straggly grey beard and a gap toothed grin revealing his few remaining nicotine stained fangs to prove he was old (to the Nozzers, very very old). Peering down he cackled "My sons, you might find it 'ard here. It is 'ard. But I promise you after this you'll never find it 'ard again". Years after, these same boys would still agree to that, although by then they were fairly certain that a regime modelled on the Royal Navy of the late nineteenth century was a little outdated in the mid-twentieth.

1. 'Nozzers' - *New boys*

Inadequate food, bare feet and the rule 'Out of sight of the Duty Officer is out of bounds' were more typical of Dickens than of post-war Britain.

After two years of this John still wanted to go to sea, but definitely not in the Royal Navy and most certainly not on its lower deck, so to the Merchant Navy he went. His training was a great help in this, but the one thing he had neither been prepared for, nor warned about was the solitude. At school and on the Mercury John had been one of a team of around thirty. He was trained at the latter to be one of a Royal Navy class of about the same number, or one of a ship's company many times that size. Nothing had prepared him for the isolation of a tramp ship with a total crew of fifty or more of whom only two or three would be anything like his own age. And because he was an Apprentice, an embryo officer, which they were not, he could not be too friendly with them anyway. This was one of the reasons why John, a gregarious soul, had only a short career in the Merchant Navy.

Chapter 4

**Bill Johnson,
Junior Apprentice**

At Sea, Saturday

Dear Mum and Dad,

As we reach Suez tomorrow I thought I had better drop you a line. I have settled down fairly well, and have now found my sea legs, although last week I was so sea sick that I wanted to die. I'm well over it now, I hope for good. I share a cabin with Rod Wilshaw, the Senior Apprentice, he's twenty and goes up for his ticket next trip. We don't have much space, most of the cabin is taken up with our bunks, I have the top one. A chest of drawers, a shared wardrobe and a day bed (you would call it a sofa) line the cabin sides. There is a hand basin in one corner, but it has no running water and it drains into a bucket, so we both use the communal bathroom most of the time. Our remaining floor space is only about five feet square - small maybe, but it has its advantages when it comes to scrubbing out. The cabin is painted white, but it is enlivened by some strips of green plasticine on the deckhead (ceiling to you). They follow along some of the seams in the plankwork that have minor leaks and they serve to lead the drips to the bulkheads (walls) down which they run harmlessly to the deck, rather than falling on to the coir matting carpet below.

I am on day work, starting at eight o'clock, finishing at five, with an hour for lunch. Our first job on leaving port was to wash down; iron ore dust gets everywhere and until you have experienced it you would not believe it. Although we kept our ports[1] screwed down all the time, there was still a layer of purple dust

1. Ports - *Portholes, in this connection, of the type which hinge inwards to open and screw closed*

over all my shirts every time I opened a drawer. After washing down, half of us overhauled the derrick gear, the others started chipping. The Mate reckons to paint the ship from end to end each voyage, and so every part has to be chipped or scraped, red leaded and painted. So far I have only been allowed to tackle the chipping bit, the ABs do all the more interesting jobs.

Rod is on the Mate's watch, the four to eight. He is off officially from eight in the morning until four in the afternoon, but on a short trip like this the Mate has most of the watch below out on overtime, so Rod works alongside me on deck all day as well. As one of the watch he takes his turn at the wheel and he has promised to have me up in the wheelhouse to teach me to steer once we clear the Med.

The food is OK, at least there is plenty of it, but Doc (that's what the Cook is called at sea) isn't quite up to your standards, Mum. There's stacks of meat and fish, but very little in the way of fresh vegetables and no fruit at all. The milk is tinned evaporated milk mixed with water, we call it 'shaky milk'. It's not as good as fresh milk, but much better than the sweetened condensed tins they issue to the sailors. You would also be interested in what we call our tea; it's a hot meal, stew or curry, followed by cold meat and salad. The salad was lettuce and stuff for the first couple of days, but now it's raw onion sliced up in vinegar, covered with pepper. Sometimes we get tinned beetroot as well, but not very often. Sunday meals are special too, we always have chicken for dinner, and for tea tinned salmon and chips.

I don't have much spare time in the week, most evenings after tea there is some dhobying (washing) or ironing to be done. I'm getting quite a dab hand at that now. Sometimes I do a bit of study after work, but mostly that's left to the weekend. I read quite a bit as well. There is a small library on board, about a hundred books or so, and most people have a private store of paperbacks. Saturday is a day off but in the morning I usually study and in the afternoon Rod and I have to clean up the cabin. Most weeks we need to wash the paintwork as well as scrub the deck. Sunday morning the Captain goes round on inspection. So far he hasn't found anything seriously wrong, but he did 'suggest' that we consider polishing up the drawer handles. Well when he suggests something it means it had better be done, or else.....; they really gleam now! Actually they were not too bad before, in fact I had just cleaned them, but I suppose he has to pick up something to let us know he isn't just paying a social call.

Sunday afternoon we have lifeboat drill. At about three o'clock the emergency signal is made on the siren, six short blasts, and everyone has to assemble at their lifeboat station wearing a lifejacket. We don't actually launch the boats, usually we don't even take their covers off, but we still have to do it once a week. Last week the Captain decided that we would swing one out as it was flat calm, but it was nearly a disaster. First the davits would not swing and it took

Chippy with his sledge hammer to sort that out; then the boat almost went straight over the side when one of the firemen let go the wrong rope. This drill is called 'Board of Trade Sports' and it can certainly live up to its name.

The weather is good. It is now warm enough to work on deck without a shirt and I have got quite a good tan. It's not too hot yet, but when we reach the Red Sea it should really warm up. They say you never stop sweating for a whole week, night and day; but then they also said that you could never cross the Bay of Biscay without meeting a full gale, so I expect I shall survive somehow.

By the way, the three piece uniform that the company insisted I needed was rather a waste. I wore it on the train from Euston to Glasgow, but since then the trousers and waistcoat have remained on a wire coat hanger in the wardrobe. I did wear the jacket for meals in the saloon until we reached Gib, but since then it has been too warm and the jacket is now on the hanger too.

Well I must close now if I am going to post this, not in a mail box with a stamp, but give it to the Chief Steward who is closing the mail in an hour's time. He will send it ashore with the ship's agent when we reach Port Said. All being well we should then go straight on through the Canal to our next stop, for coaling at Aden.

Give my regards to all at Home, and tell John not to worry too much, I'm sure he'll get through his examination with no trouble at all.

Love from Bill

Chapter 5

**Alex McGovan,
Chief Steward**

'....and some have greatness thrust upon them.' For some it may be the absolute greatness of kingship, for most the relative greatness of less grand stations. To Alex McGovan the glory hole[1] steward from a Glasgow tenement, it was the office of Chief Steward on the Atlantic Wanderer, a seven thousand tonner tramping from London. This greatness had come late in life. Ten years previously at forty, Alex had been an unkempt, balding little man, seldom completely free from the grease of his job, especially under the edges of his bitten finger nails. His spells ashore were spent in the public bars of Southampton, his only contact with the opposite sex their barmaids. Yet somehow, from this improbable background, he had struck up a friendship with a plump and respectable middle aged spinster, who earned her living as a copy typist in a solicitor's office in Winchester and spent her leisure time singing in the local chapel choir. It was a true case of opposites attracting, and how they ever first met remained a mystery, but the friendship blossomed and in due course the homely spinster became Mrs. McGovan. This gave her a greatly increased status in her own circle and in return she determined to do the same for her husband.

The first steps were easy enough. There was a waiting list for the cushy jobs on the liners, but the occasional requirements of the few cargo vessels calling at Southampton were always difficult to fill. So it was not hard to get Alex off the Queens and on to a London Greek. It was a step upwards from the glory hole to Assistant Steward, although it meant a drop in the take home pay. Then by carefully planned stages, which included correspondence courses in English and arithmetic, Mrs. McGovan slowly but surely shaped her husband for higher things. To many, the ambition to become the Second Steward of a tramp ship might seem no ambition at

1. Glory hole - *The stewards quarters on a passenger liner*

19

all, but to Alex with his youthful background and late start upwards, it represented the near impossible, beyond which Chief Steward was clearly unachievable. Nevertheless, thanks to the persistence of his wife, he made Second Steward. When he was turned fifty, the Chief Steward had to be put ashore in in Gibraltar on the way home with suspected appendicitis. This lucky chance pitchforked Alex into the Chief Steward's slot as a temporary measure and somehow he managed to hang on to it. He was still a balding little man, but no longer the greasy unkempt figure of his bachelor days.

The outward conversion was complete; Alex McGovan had become the cynosure of the middle aged nine to five gentlemen of Mrs. McGovan's chapel. He mixed well with them, the bespoke tailoring Mrs. McGovan persuaded him to wear blended into the upper echelons of their dark suited ranks, and he stood out in their gatherings by virtue of what seemed to them the exciting profession of seafaring. The good lady's cup was full to overflowing; she had the only status symbols valued by the ladies of the chapel; a good husband and a nice home of her own - things she had dreamt about, but never expected to achieve as she had watched her rather colourless youth inexorably sliding towards a drab elderly spinsterhood.

Alex also gained. He much preferred his new found respectability to his previous existence and when compared to his Glaswegian upbringing it represented the ultimate. The idea of living in one of a neat row of suburban homes had never entered his head, and he now owned one, albeit on a mortgage. As well as his gratitude to his wife, which he repaid with devotion, he felt almost as great a debt to his employers which he repaid by giving them good value, but it was hard work. As Chief Steward he was in sole charge of the ship's providore department. Not only did he have to supervise a staff of three Stewards, two Cooks and a galley Boy, he had also to order and account for all the food consumed by a crew of nearly fifty. Most Chief Stewards had some specialist training for this latter task, but Alex had none. His first few trips had been a nightmare.

Not only was his newly acquired arithmetic unsure, but the English he had to use in his reports was a comparatively untried skill. Many a night he had experienced the sleepless frustration of being unable to keep his expenditure within its set limits and an inability to unscramble his unbalancable accounts. These moments were invariably followed by an early morning sick feeling of hopelessness in the pit of his stomach, which persisted as he began work again, with no more hope of success than on the previous day. He had no respite at all; the ship ground remorselessly on towards her next port of call, with her crew consuming ever more food and creating new problems to add to his already insoluble backlog.

Fortunately Mrs. McGovan was aware of his dilemma and was always on the quayside when the ship docked at the voyage's end. In his first year as Chief Steward Alex almost never saw home, he and his wife worked virtually non-stop night and day to sort out one trip's accounts before sailing on the next. Somehow between the two of them they got away with it, but it was often a close call. Had the ship been away from a home port for more than three months during this period they would certainly never have managed it. It was a situation that could not last, the strain was far too great, and had it not been for his wife's encouragement Alex would have given up very early on. However very gradually the separate problems began to repeat themselves, and instead of compounding the chaos, solutions used once before began to fall into place. New solutions were evolved from the old by trial and error, learned by rote and finally committed to paper in the exercise book which accompanied Alex wherever he went. In this way he built up a reference system that although neither infallible nor foolproof, did work most of the time. Any fresh problem was categorised as 'That happened in Sydney last trip' or 'The last of the potatoes we bought in Dakar went rotten after ten days' or whatever. This would trigger off a frantic search for the right page in the right exercise book. There were check-off lists to be raised with the ship's chandlers; quantities to be ordered per man per day; alternative supplies when root vegetables cost more than he was prepared to authorise and many others. Alex used these notes to help form his decisions, but it was his constant recourse to them that truly kept his hard won knowledge constantly under review and thus instantly available.

They were also instrumental in earning him the respect of the agents and suppliers. He was always aware of what any transaction had cost in the past and insisted on a full explanation of any changes. These he duly noted down in their presence for future reference; a procedure which ensured that he was rarely, if ever cheated. So even if he was not sharp enough to obtain the best bargains, he was too well informed to fall for the worst, and overall his performance was certainly no worse than that of any other Chief Steward in the company. His working life was still at times a progression from crisis to crisis. It would be many more years before Alex was able to foresee and avoid them, but by calling on previously tried strategies he was able to resolve most problems as they arose, and no longer had to face each morning sick with worry over those he could not solve yesterday.

This then was Alex McGovan, Chief Steward of the Atlantic Wanderer by normal standards a very ordinary man doing a commonplace task with an average degree of competence - but to Alex it was a greatness thrust upon him, which he strove his modest best to justify.

Chapter 6

Phil Boston,
Deck Boy

Some things you just have to put up with mused Phil, as yet another chunk of icy, foul smelling mud slithered under his collar and down his back. Deck Boys always got the worst jobs, and in a ship as old as this it would have been surprising indeed if the chain locker was self stowing. Down there in the dark and slime the only light was provided by the chain pipe, through which deluged the muddy water hosed off the anchor chain. This job was unpleasant, and like very few others onboard, not without an element of danger. The cable links were always slimy underfoot and if you slipped your shouts could never have been heard above the windlass clanking away on the fo'c'sle. So you just handled the chain so that you did not slip, taking care to spread it evenly, as any piled up links could crash down on your ankles with bone shattering force at any time. The risks were always present, but not the freezing unpleasantness; in the tropics cold salt water would have been quite bearable, but this was the Thames in midwinter. There were plenty of ports with sweeter smelling mud too! Anyway, as soon as the anchor was home he could disappear aft for a hot shower as he had no further duties on deck and did not have to wet the tea for another couple of hours. This stand down was not a reward for his work in the chain locker, but simply because dinner was not for another two hours. As junior Deck Boy Phil was the Peggy, the crew's mess man, and his main tasks were to collect the crew's meals, brew their smokoe tea or coffee, wash up after them and generally keep the mess room clean.

It was not much of a training in seamanship. In fact his only seamanlike duties were in entering and leaving harbour; in the cable locker if there was any anchor work, otherwise standing behind the AB on the windlass drum, coiling down the six inch manila mooring ropes. Still it would only be a couple more trips before he became senior Deck Boy. Then, like his mate Frank, he would work days with the bosun and really learn some seamanship, as was proved by the sheath knife now proudly slung on Frank's belt. It was Phil's second trip so he had this at least to look forward to in the fairly near future. Scrubbing mess tables was very definitely not what he had signed on for.

Sometimes he wondered exactly what he had signed on for. Most of the lads he knew in the terraced houses of his Birkenhead home had come to sea as the only alternative to dull routine jobs in factories, but not Phil Boston. His passion had always been football, right from his earliest games in the street. Some of his first childhood memories were of Mums and Dads sunning themselves in armchairs on the flat roof of a street air raid shelter while the kids played football in the street below, and of the way they scattered, parents and children alike, when the occasional policeman was sighted. At school he had always been the leader of the playground kick arounds, and later the star of various youth club teams. He had even been good enough to get a trial with a league club; the offer of a playing apprenticeship after National Service had been mentioned. But somehow things had not worked out, Phil had chosen the freer life of the Merchant Navy rather than uniformed National Service, only to discover later that two years was not enough, and that to avoid going into khaki he would have to remain at sea until he was twenty-six. He could of course leave and then do his two years National Service, but that would make him nineteen at the very least, and the club had only mentioned schemes for eighteen year olds. Still, perhaps, he might see them about it after the next trip - a promise he was to go on making to himself voyage after voyage until it was far too late.

For the moment he had to content himself with the ship's football team; almost every ship had one, most had a football, some even a set of shirts. The problem was always boots and usually half the team had to play in plimsolls. It did not really matter though, they only played against other ships with the same problems, and never on pitches good enough for lack of gear to affect the standard of play. Phil played centre half as well as being captain and self-appointed fixtures secretary, which was something of a chore. Not only did he have to find the pitch and the opponents, he also had to cajole the younger seamen, firemen, mates and engineers into giving up valued drinking time to play, but he felt it well worth the effort just to get a game. On this last trip things had been easier, they had been stuck on the Australian coast during one of the perennial coal strikes, and a side effect had been a beer shortage. The crews of the ships finding time lying heavy on their hands had, at the insistence of the padre of the local Missions to Seamen, formed a league, with fixtures and proper referees. Although the results had been inconclusive Phil's ship had been well on the way to the top of the league, until the end of the strike and replenishment of beer stocks in the pubs immediately put an end to any further thoughts of football.

Most Deck Boys were more or less ignored by the rest of the crew, but his footballing connections made Phil something of a celebrity, and so the crowd had decided to show him the ropes. It started in the 'Iron Duke' next to the dock gates, not five minutes from home. The first pint went down quite easily; by the third Phil was a man among men, slapping everyone on the back and laughing uproariously at every joke; after that, quite unaccountably, he kept knocking glasses off the table no matter how carefully he controlled his movements. Then, suddenly, he felt ill, very ill, and only just made it to the toilet. He could not remember getting back to the ship, but he could remember the wrenching pain in his gut as he was sick again and again throughout the night. The following morning the approving smiles as he gagged over a mug of black coffee convinced him that despite the most god-awful hangover, he had arrived.

However this was only the opening stage in his education. The ship's first port of call was to be Bone in Algeria, to load iron ore, and all the way out Phil was promised, with many a knowing wink, that the run ashore to the 'Black Cat' would really be something. So he steeled himself for another session of too much beer, to be followed by further griping stomach pains as the after effect. It was part of the code that he never for one moment considered not going ashore as one of the boys.

It was true, as promised the visit to the 'Black Cat' was like nothing else he had ever experienced. For one thing the crew took far more pains over their appearance than for a run ashore to an English pub; Brylcreme and after-shave were in great demand in the bathroom. All were in their best rig and obviously on their best behaviour. The 'Black Cat' was not like an English pub either, it was all beaded curtains and shaded lights, with a strange oriental aroma - actually Gauloises smoke instead of Woodbines, but Phil was not to know this. There were more girls than in English pubs too, and they seemed to know all the crew. They were much more friendly than English girls and in next to no time they were sitting on the men's laps eagerly helping them to get through a fair amount of drink. Phil also noticed that pairs disappeared from time to time, returning shortly afterwards to the accompaniment of sly laughter and good humoured banter. Phil joined in this, but it was not until a rather overweight girl seated herself on his lap and began to wriggle suggestively that he at last realised what sort of a bar this might be.

Her 'Jiggy, Jiggy? You like short time, Johnny?' made him flush scarlet and feel hot all over. The encouraging leers of his mates did nothing to ease his embarrassment. It was not that Phil was not interested in girls, but this one did not attract him at all, she was too old and too buxom. In fact she reminded him somehow of his Auntie May back in Birkenhead, not of the alluring sylph-like naked houris of his erotic fantasies. Anyway besides being embarrassed he was distinctly uncomfortable; the girl knew her trade, and Phil was certainly physically aroused, but she was too weighty by far for the slightly built Deck Boy. Her generous right buttock, naked under its flimsy robe, was placed directly on a very sensitive portion of his anatomy, and if she did not move pretty damn quick Phil felt it would break off. In such a dire emergency there was only one thing he could do, so with a violent heave he deposited all twelve stone of her on the floor, to the huge enjoyment of his audience. Phil clearly remembered the next three things; first the squishy thump, rather like wet fish on a slab, as the now uncovered behind contacted the stone floor; next the tremendous feeling of relief as the excruciating pain ceased and his crumpled member resurrected itself through his unbuttoned fly; and lastly the stinging slap as the girl's beringed fingers hit his cheek as she flounced off through the beaded screen, furious not with the humiliation of her revealed charms, but with the choler of financial loss.

As the still virgin Deck Boy returned to the ship he consoled himself with the thought that if, as fo'c'sle lore acknowledged 'You aren't a man until you've had a dose', then he was quite content to remain a boy, at least until next trip.

Chapter 7

**John Jones,
Fireman Trimmer**

'Falstaffian' was the only possible description, for like his knightly namesake, John Jones had a truly tremendous girth with a rumbustious belly laugh and a prodigious thirst to match. Whilst others might go boozing and whoring, John's shoregoing was well worthy of those goodly Elizabethan terms 'roistering' and 'wenching'. In his cups this man became more boisterous, his humour rising in direct proportion to the drink taken and the noise around him; overflowing cups, great guffaws, discordant singing, it was all one. Should there be a brawl, so much the better, for he would be in the centre of it. His sheer exuberance was as often that which started it, as it was his high good humour that kept fisticuffs from becoming knives and broken bottles. After such bouts it was an even chance whether John would roll back aboard or spend the night as a guest of the local constabulary.

These skirmishes he treated as part of the rich fabric of life, his great delight was to recount the choicest ones. One of these favourites was a simple Drunk and Disorderly on New Year's Eve. If, and only if, you were at least half drunk it was side splitting to hear John mimic the Magistrates sanctimonious tones of regret over his first customer of the New Year, and the pain it gave His Honour to see a man sink so low, so often, but pious concern was briskly replaced by a business like dismissal that relieved the Fireman of a customary five pounds.

Another item of the repertoire featured a public convenience in Middlesborough. It had been for John a quiet night, a dozen pints or so, no brawls and a steady stagger shipward to bed. It was this stagger that started the trouble, one of its involuntary arabesques finishing up against the rough brickwork of a building. He then realised that he was fair game for any passing constable, and that he was too

26

broke to meet the subsequently inevitable fine. So deeming discretion the better part of valour John decided to retire within the building rather than to court arrest, for the brickwork supporting his slumped frame had the welcoming lighted sign, 'Gentlemen'. It would he knew from previous experience be a longish wait, so placing his penny in the slot, and hitching his belt more comfortably about his girth he prepared to sit it out. Even at his best John was no rapid thinker. In his present state thoughts had to traverse his brain very slowly, and in single file to have any chance at all. Thus it was that some time later on emerging from an uneasy doze the sight of the tiled walls hazily became his first awareness of his surroundings, an impression which did not have time enough to be fully processed before the next, which should have been an alert message referring to his still be-trousered state, but alas no warning signal was telegraphed from brain to bowel. Thus on this night although neither arrested nor fined he was certainly not singing joyfully when eventually he slunk his unfragrant way back on board.

For this exuberant giant of a Welshman drinking was always a joyful exercise. He could never understand those puritanical countries where such a pleasurable occupation had to be indulged in silently or sedately. In Australia and New Zealand he could never fathom why such otherwise reasonable people could tolerate their joyless 6 p.m. pub closing, he could drink with the best of the Aussies or Kiwis but could never even take the edge off his thirst within the permitted time limit. Still there were always places like Jimmy Gleason's at the back of the yacht harbour in Auckland where the writ of the law did not run for thirsty merchant seamen. Normally such bars were left well alone by the police providing that both drinking and brawling were unobtrusively kept behind closed doors, but whenever John was in town his rowdy enjoyment could hardly be so constrained. To the Antipodean Police and Judiciary it was a provocative flouting of their own reasonable laws by a Bloody Pom. His fines down under were more severe than those at home and far more frequent, he had even been kept in cells overnight and missed his ship on more than one occasion.

John's stories could be heard on board, but more often they were reserved for the bar of his home village set in the heart of the valleys. Here among the grandeur of the mountains and the desecration of the spoil tips John had been born, and here he returned between voyages. In the smoke filled, pine varnished bar among the miners his stories were exotically outlandish, but no more so than the Welsh he now spoke would have been to his shipmates. Here John had grown from boyhood into a world that knew but one trade - coal. The mining dominated their working lives, as its slag heaps did their homes. With all this it was as inevitable that coal should claim John as it had his family before him. Even when he made his break away to sea it was still the coal that won and he became a Fireman Trimmer. Whilst the sea had done little to blunt his Welsh accent it had greatly sharpened his thirst. He left his valleys a slender youth with a steady walk; he returned a veritable giant with a seaman's rolling gait and a fund of tales that made him a local celebrity.

As the sea had given John his fame as a storyteller in the valleys, so the valleys in their turn gave him something back. Others could only find the true quality of coal by burning it, but to the Welshman it was like soil to the countryman; too much sheen bespoke poor steaming, too rich a tarry smell foretold coagulating clinker: it was as though the very cobs spoke to him, telling him from which corner of the principality they hailed and how well they would serve the ships that burnt them. Foreign coals spoke too in tongues that he understood but could never respect. This arcane fund of knowledge was sometimes called upon by the Chief Engineer if the quality of the bunkers delivered did not appear to be of the quality invoiced, John's advice perhaps enabling the Chief to get a fairer price. This had the advantage of making the Chief more tolerant of the after effects of John's bacchanalian runs ashore, otherwise they might have earned the Fireman many a logging[1].

---

1. Logging - *Offences recorded in the ship's Log Book, for which the Captain could impose fines*

Chapter 8

Max Kershaw,
The One That Got Away

The story of the retired sailorman is not new. He placed an oar on his shoulder and marched off inland; eventually deep in the countryside a rustic asked him the use of his strange burden. It was here that he settled down and made his home. The story does not say whether he was happy with his decision. Max Kershaw on the other hand had, metaphorically, picked up his oar far away from salt water, intending to carry it until he found himself amongst those who knew its true purpose.

His preparations had been long and thorough. His earliest school memories were of the National Savings 'Warships Week'; then the corridors had been emblazoned with Norman Wilkinson posters of battleships, convoys and bronzed figures with blue uniforms and grimly determined expressions. He still had some of them, surreptitiously removed all those years ago, dog eared but still cherished schoolboy mementoes. For the rest of the class it had been a nine day wonder and they quickly reverted to their normal lives as embryo cowboys or Spitfire pilots. Max however still remained the last man to leave his sinking command, that is whenever he could be spared from his topgallant yard swaying off the gale swept Horn. By his eleventh birthday he had read and re-read every book in the local library that had any mention of the sea or seafaring. He also knew the recruiting standards by heart; height, educational qualifications and, distressingly, minimum age. He still had another five whole years to wait. He consoled himself that next March he could join the Sea Cadet Corps, one step nearer his goal.

For that year time seemed to stand still, but it passed at last, and the Sea Cadets filled his next years. At weekends he learned to handle boats under oars, sail and power. In school holidays he went away with the navy on courses, training to be a cadet gunner, cook, naval airman, telegraphist and even a PTI. Between times there were two parades a week where he learned knotting, splicing and other nautical skills of little obvious use in his industrial Midland home town, clearly vital on salt water. He was fully competent to take the required action should he ever come across two steam vessels meeting end on or nearly end on; if ever he encountered a vessel temporarily not under command he would have been happy to advise her master on the appropriate signal to be hoisted; but such events never took place when he was walking along the High Street. He was determined to look the part too; his boots gleamed, his lanyard sparkled, and his hair was always cropped to regulation bristliness about neck and ears. He even practiced his own private version of the true matelot's roll, but only secretly before his bedroom mirror, never in public.

During all these years his keenness for all things nautical never wavered, but slowly he veered away from the Royal Navy as he realised that as well as serving on ships he would also have to spend some time in shore establishments. It was even possible to meet naval ratings who had never served at sea! On the other hand no one had ever heard of merchant seamen not being on ships; in their navy there were no shore appointments, it was all sea time. So although he rose rapidly from AB through Leading Cadet to Cadet Petty Officer he was by the age of sixteen confirmed in his resolve to join the Merchant Navy.

His last six months ashore passed in an exciting whirl; important looking letters in brown envelopes, interviews, kitting up and finally the journey to his first ship, from Euston by the Midnight Scot, wearing for the first time in his life a stiff white collar. This last was a mistaken vanity, for not only was it uncomfortable, but tie, collar and stud all had lives of their own. All the way to Glasgow one or the other would stray from their appointed place and long before arrival the pristine starched whiteness was patterned with faint greasy prints from sweating frustrated fingertips.

This for Max was only the first of many frustrations. He had trained long and hard for the right to hoist his metaphoric oar upon his shoulder. He had headed for the sea but the oar was to remain unrecognised. Real oars were present on board, but not for use; they were securely lashed under the canvas covers of the lifeboats. Most of the other tools and impedimenta of the seaman's trade were present, but to Max they seemed little used. The lead and line which he had taken long hours to master was there, correctly marked, but wound on a spindle and left neglected at the back of a bridge locker. There was rigging; but it was supplied ready spliced and set up by dry dock riggers, the only ship board task was its periodic greasing. Even the anchors and mooring ropes so seamanlike to handle in small boats were here so large that they had to be manipulated at second hand by steam power. After a short while Max felt that all the seamanship required of him was the ability to handle a sugee[1] wad, a chipping hammer or a paint brush; very necessary, but he could equally well have learned all this ashore in the building trade with his father. Even at sea the steady mechanical throb of the ship's engines had little of the life you could feel transmitted through the fabric of the small boats he longed to handle once more. Masefield might

1. Sugee - *Hindustani word for the soft soap solution used to wash paintwork*

speak of the kick of the wheel, but he had served mostly in sailing ships. Even in a full gale with the ship's head falling violently off course in the trough of each successive wave the telemotor steering gear was as dead and lifeless in his hands as the wheel on his mother's mangle at home.

However Max had been pursuing his ambition for far too many years to admit defeat this easily. The sea had been the same since time immemorial, and he just would not believe the ways of seamen could have changed so completely. It took him two full years to concede finally that the romance and glamour he craved were no longer to be found on the steel cargo carriers of the modern merchant navy. A lesser man might have been broken, but not Max Kershaw. After serving this appointed apprenticeship at sea he shouldered his oar yet again to continue his search; but a two year National Service stint in an administrative shore billet in the Royal Navy proved to be a step even further away from the true seagoing he sought.

The next time he followed more closely in the footsteps of the mythical retired sailor, retreating deep inland, far away from the sound of the sea, and there in the building trade alongside his father he laid down his oar for good. The wheel has come full circle; Max is now in command of the Sea Cadet Unit in which he served as a boy, and as nearly as possible in a non-nautical Midland suburb he has achieved his true vocation, teaching boys to be seafarers; but only in the evenings, at weekends and during holidays.

Chapter 9

Corporal Dan Bell,
Fireman Trimmer

I was sure that there was something vaguely familiar about the sea boots, beard, heavy blue sweater and rolling gait that made the figure on the beach more nautical than the saltiest of sea dogs. The image was not accidental but carefully tailored to boost trade. So too was the rather loud, forcedly jolly 'yo-ho-ho' voice with which he cracked risque jokes with the young matrons or told the most outrageously improbable sea stories to their offspring. Clearly he was a favourite among the seaside visitors and the trim condition of his rowing boats - "Fifty pence per hour, children half price" - indicated a degree of modest prosperity.

Despite all this there was an indefinable something that, to a professional, marked him as a landsman who would be out of place in anything bigger than a rowing boat, or farther out to sea than the end of the pier. He handled his boats competently but without the innate skill of the true seaman. Anyone observant enough to notice all of this would have been quite right. Dan Bell was not a seaman; he was in business. His brother-in-law, Harry, an ex-trawlerman, spent the summer taking parties fishing for mackerel off the Point. Dan handled the shore side and the rowing boats. Their wives ran the family guest house. It was a comfortable enough venture and whilst he was quite content to live by the sea, Dan had no desire at all to live on it. Dan had however been to sea, just once, some twenty years before.

Like many other school leavers in the immediate post war era, the prospect of National Service completely blocked out any thought of starting a lifelong career. Dan supposed that, like his father, he would get a job in a factory; maintenance, carpentry probably, for he was good with his hands, and had a fair chance of a job, but only when he had completed his two years. The army changed his world. For the first time he lived away from an industrial town and sampled the freedom of open space, trees, grass and sunlight. After that any return to a factory was just unthinkable. So, demobbed with the rank of corporal, Dan headed for the widest, openest space he could find - Australia. Again he was typical of many of his generation. National Service had shown them how to look after themselves, but not taught them a trade. It had shown them that the world was not all smoke filled cities surrounded by uninspiring stereotyped suburbs, but not how to become part of that other world. Many succumbed to the inducements of the several Commonwealth countries who at that time were creaming off young men with ten pound assisted passages. So Dan arrived jobless in Australia.

For most this was the start of a new life; but for a minority, Dan amongst them, it was just the mixture as before. An unskilled man has only the same limited range of jobs open to him in any country of the world. Some few filtered back home on British ships, replacements for the steady drain of seamen who, preferring the life overseas, jumped ship before leaving the coast, thus freeing berths for those returning emigres for whom the attractions of Australia failed to outweigh its disillusionments; and so Dan Bell went to sea.

To everyone on board he was 'The Corporal', a nickname originally bestowed because the only working shirts he possessed were khaki drill shirts with their two stripes still in place. It stuck because even as his khaki stood out from the faded blues of all his shipmates so did his bearing mark him out a landsman. He moved about the deck with a stiffish precision, totally dissimilar to the loose rolling gait of the others, and to his marked disadvantage in rough weather. Then the Corporal was forever stubbing his toes and barking his shins on the various fittings that the rolling ship continuously placed in the paths of the unwary, whereas the apparently careless shambling of the seafarers left them unscathed. Towards the end of the trip this was not so noticeable; sheer self preservation started Dan's military bearing on the downward path towards the rollicking walk he affected in his later seaside years.

As an untrained man Dan was at first put on deck under the eye of the dayworkers, but two days out one of the firemen succumbed to heat exhaustion, grossly exaggerated by too many prolonged sessions on cheap Australian plonk. So for the rest of the trip the Corporal was transferred to the engine room. Possibly with his leaning towards the wide open spaces, a complete trip on deck might have kept him at sea, but the stokehold was a very different proposition. Down below it was cramped and almost completely airless. The gloom, continually lit by the searing red glow of opened furnace doors had a certain Dantesque grandeur, but the choking clouds of coal dust, smoke and powdered clinker reduced it to a hellish four hour penance to be endured twice daily. Dan never learned to come to terms with this, he found himself continuously gasping for air so hot that it threatened to burn out his lungs at the very moment when his maximum strength was required to throw coal deep into the gaping red maw of the fire box. There was an art in this that the other Firemen had acquired through long habituation; either their lungs were immune to the heat and dust, or they had learned the trick of breathing before making a too close approach to the boilers. Whatever it was it must have taken time to perfect for Dan never mastered it during the voyage home. There was also a knack in using the minimum muscle power when swinging a shovel. Dan never progressed beyond the back breaking dig and throw of the novice, so throughout the trip he was forced to use far more effort than was called for from the older hands. The only trick of the trade he did master was that of using a shovel without blistering his hands beyond endurance. Perhaps mastery was not the most suitable term, it was simply that in his first two weeks he blistered so much that his hands were incapable of any further injury and they became as black, seamed and horny as those of anyone else in the stokehold.

Although he never complained the work was sheer purgatory. At the end of his four hour watch all he wanted to do was to stretch out on his bunk and sleep. At times even washing and eating seemed too much effort. Still he stuck it out, but when the Second Engineer offered him a berth on the next trip Dan was more than certain that the seafaring life was not for him. Thereafter, although quite happy to live by the sea and wrest a living from its shore, he was never again tempted to venture across it.

Chapter 10

Abdul Moulay Hassan,
Ordinary Seaman

"Quarter turn to port, two spokes starboard, steer one four five." The first wheel handed over to his relief the amount of helm needed to hold the ship on her track, and the course to steer. "Course One Four Five, Sir." was reported to the Third mate and answered by a grunt from the monkey island[1]. The off duty helmsman clattered on down the ladder and for a brief moment the sound of his footsteps receded down the deck. Seconds later the Third returned to the bridge deck and the chartroom door banged gently behind him as he settled down to work out the compass error, leaving the helmsman alone with his thoughts. It was a peaceful tropical night, the clear sky sprinkled with myriads of stars and with scarcely a puff of air coming through the opened wheelhouse window. The gently swaying compass card had a soporific effect, but the man at the wheel remained alert enough to check the ship's drift whenever the lubber line slid past 243° one side or 247° the other. If you corrected before that the ship would just chase her own tail, and the snake-like wake would cause the Third Mate to appear in the doorway growling under his breath "How's your head?". If you corrected later you might drift well off course. It was a warm night and by heaven he needed a cigarette. Furtively, for smoking at the wheel was not allowed, he reached into his dungaree pocket for a smoke, and held the lighted cigarette carefully in his cupped hand. Although the smell of the tobacco was sufficient to give the game away, it was a long recognised custom that if the glow could not be seen then no one caused a fuss. The beams overhead were thick with the old cigarette ends that bore witness to this, it being another mutually observed tradition that the blind eye would remain turned so long as cigarette ash was not left all over the wheelhouse deck.

Abdul preferred these quiet night watches when he could be by himself and think. He was not anti-social by nature but found himself set somewhat apart from

1. Monkey Island - *A platform on the wheelhouse roof on which the main Standard Compass was mounted so as to be as remote as possible from the ship's magnetic influence and to give an all round view for taking bearings*

his shipmates on two counts; firstly by race, for he was an Arab among a predominantly West Indian deck crew; secondly by upbringing. He could perhaps have mixed more freely with the firemen for they were Arabs to a man, but they were working class whilst Abdul was definitely a member of the educated middle class, and in no way free from its petty snobberies. His upbringing in Aden had been strict but comfortable. His father, an official with the government, had been able to provide a good education for all his sons, but was not quite affluent enough to afford the place at Cairo University that had been Abdul's dream. In Aden there were few openings for an intelligent lad outside the government service. This Abdul had rejected, like so many sons the world over, for no other reason than that it was his father's career, and that he, Abdul, intended to do better. There were many discussions among the menfolk of the family before it was decided that Abdul could leave Aden with his father's blessing, which was essential because without it filial duty would have prevented him leaving at all.

In order to save money as much as to prove his independence Abdul decided that his leave taking should be a self supporting activity, so he signed on the first ship out of Aden that was short of a man, and finished up in a cheap lodging house in Tiger Bay. Here among the Arab community he had made his home for the past three years, although 'Home' was a somewhat misleading term. The periods between voyages were short and infrequent. Abdul did not keep his room on while he was at sea and all his possessions travelled with him in a pair of battered fibre suitcases.

Ambition he still had but it was somewhat vague. He definitely wanted to do or be something significant and he was saving hard to that end but did not quite know where to start. Certainly it was not a life at sea. British ships generally tramped to countries where his skin stood Abdul at a disadvantage and most certainly his horizons were broader than his shared cabin in the fo'c'sle (although now down aft the seamen's quarters were still so called). Abdul had first signed as a Deck Boy in Aden but that was three years ago. Now he was rated Ordinary Seaman and would very shortly sit for his EDH ticket and then after another four years be rated AB. He wanted this not so much for the advanced status as for the higher wages, which would enable him to increase his allotment to the Seamen's Savings Bank - a specialist agency of the National Savings movement catering exclusively for seafarers which accepted monthly allotments against wages.

This trip he had something special to look forward to. After discharging coal in Rio the ship was due to load salt in Spain for Japan. This would mean a bunkering call in Aden and he had not seen his family since he first left home. When the coaling stages were rigged in Aden the gangs of dusky figures began to pass the hundredweight wicker baskets from the scows[1] up over the ship's side and into the bunkers, chanting the while in unison. Rapidly the ship and everything on it disappeared under a cloud of black dust. This made the appearance of the dignified

1. Scows - *Local barges used for lightering cargo between ship and shore*

figure on the deck even more startling. He wore gleaming snowy white robes from which a patriarchal face glared out with piercing brown eyes. He was attended by two obsequious servants and quite obviously commanded respect from all the Arab workers. They even stopped handling coal so that the minimum of dust should soil his clothes. This was a mark of respect definitely not shown to the Captain; coal was artlessly dumped to create an even denser black pall whenever he appeared in his shore going whites. The old gentleman looked around with a rather distasteful expression and stalked off aft. Here his expression assumed a distinctly disdainful aspect as he viewed the sailors quarters. It softened, but only very slightly, when he greeted his son, for this was Abdul's father.

As a special concession Abdul was allowed shore leave all the time the ship was in Aden, a full thirty-six hours, and he was not required back on board until 1800 Thursday, two hours before sailing. From the ship Abdul, in his shore going suit was seen standing next to his white robed father at the stern of a hired launch, but it was our last sight of him. Sailing time arrived, but no Abdul. The Harbour Police were duly notified that one seaman had jumped ship, something that happened in the barren port of Aden about as often as a snowstorm. As it was not possible to sign on an extra hand at such short notice, the Bosun had to give up his one dayworker to cover the eight to twelve watch, but apart from that the routine was little affected.

That was the end of Abdul's short career as a seaman, but it has two postscripts. The first, a stilted formal letter in rather pedantic English addressed to the Captain.

Honoured Sir,
*   I do not consider conditions on your ship are suited at all to a gentleman of my son's upbringing. Be pleased to consider his contract with you at an end. He will remain in Aden forthwith.*
*   Your respected servant,*
*   Abdul Raschid Hassan,*
*   Executive Officer, Her Majesty's Government, Aden.*

The second postscript was not to be written for another twenty years: 'Aden, Thursday, from Our Special Correspondent. British troops were again attacked last night whilst patrolling the Crater District. Shots were exchanged, a guerrilla leader thought to be Abdul Moulay Hassan was killed. British troops sustained one casualty.'

Few of his ex-shipmates would remember Abdul, fewer would have recognised his full name in print, and it is likely that none of them at all would have read this snippet of news or made the connection.

Chapter 11

**Albert Costina,
Second Cook**

Albert was universally known as 'Nookie', a slang word gained in his native Glasgow, for despite the surname of Costino, Albert was a product of a Gorbals tenement through and through. Nookie is an omnibus term referring to anything concerning the female sex, from men who are interested in it, through ladies that do, right down to those portions of their anatomy with which they do it; its exact meaning being defined by the context. Albert did all in his power to live up to his nickname. It would not be untrue to say that his one passion in life was to enjoy sex as often and in as many ways as possible and like a true afficionado his only reason for working was to provide the money and opportunity to indulge his chosen obsession.

His great grandfather had set up home close to John Brown's Glasgow shipyard when Bilbao's yards fell silent at the turn of the century, and with his Latin good looks he had wowed the local lassies, looks and tastes inherited by his offspring and by their's in due course. Albert had the dark curling hair, black pencil thin moustache, slim figure and slick grooming of the currently favoured movie stars, which, whilst warning some women to keep well clear, proved irresistible to enough of them to ensure Albert could have his way with the frequency and variety he craved.

It had not always been so. School, with its amateurish fumblings in darkened chalk smelling corridors had been irksomely restrictive from his very earliest stirrings of puberty. Equally frustrating had been adolescence, with crowded public parks in summer and the never secluded passages of his tenement home in winter. In fact to satisfy his youthful cravings he would undoubtedly have rushed into early marriage had it not been for Maggie. A generous woman in her mid-thirties she had clearly seen the promise in young Albert, and with her own man being so often away at sea had decided to take Albert in hand, and his education as well. Most women have some talent in such matters, but then, two generations before the Permissive Society, it was rarely allowed to blossom. However Maggie's sexual drive was in its full passionate flower. To say she opened Albert's eyes would do her an injustice, unclad she opened for him worlds hitherto unknown. Under her carefully uninhibited guidance the rather gloomy tenement bedroom became an Aladin's cave with open sesame earth moving heights of physical ecstasy. A classicist might have likened her to Cleopatra, but to Albert she was just Maggie and all woman. Many times in the glorious sensuality of entwined satiated bodies he felt that here all life began and ended, but his practical Eve whispered unashamedly in his ear that hers was not the only world to conquer, and besides her own Jack was due back from sea next week-end.

This withdrawal of physical gratification had a profound effect on Albert. It was he who should be coming back to the haven of her nakedly inviting body, not Jack. He would not be prudently set to one side whilst the returning sailor enjoyed the pleasures Albert felt were his by right of conquest. Such was the impetuosity of youth that, despite Maggie's discretion, it became necessary for Albert to get away, very far away from Glasgow and in a very great hurry.

For this and for no other reason he sought refuge at sea, and the sea did not let him down. Although a hard mistress, demanding total abstinence between ports she also carried him away to far off places where his enjoyment was only limited by the depth of his pocket. It was a wild carefree youth, and by his late twenties he had amassed an unrivalled wealth of experience. None of the variations on the sexual theme for sale in the world's seaports came amiss to Albert Costino and his nickname was well earned. In fact so skilled did he become that he was one of the very few who actually attained the fabled seamen's accolade of a free ride. The rather faded Parisienne who returned his money had been plying her trade in Algiers for so long that, until Albert, she had quite forgotten what it was to be aroused or satisfied by a job well done.

In those parts of the World where prostitution was not legal he had equal success. Where most of the crew had to work hard for whatever was on offer the Second Cook, as he now was, had to become a master of subterfuge to keep only one woman at a time in his bunk. Sometimes he failed, thus providing his shipmates with ringside seats to demonstrations of that hell to which no fury has been likened, with at least one of the scorned being almost or totally unclothed. He found his talent in the most unlikely places too; shop assistants and bar maids were fair game for anyone, but Nookie included otherwise respectable housewives, school teachers and even once an East European Port Health Officer whilst she was on board to declare the ship free from quarantine. Dance halls and bars remained the usual pick up points for the crew, but Albert's scope was much wider, he had even been known to attend church socials with success. His conquests were not especially good looking, or young, for as Albert so sagely observed, they were not only so much more grateful, but they often knew so much more of the art as well.

Another service he provided for the crew was as unofficial pornographer, for his interest in sex included the theoretical as well as the practical. Every ship has a store of pornography, augmented in any port that allows such freedom to its press. It is passed from hand to hand until all the better pictures have been transferred to the private collections on the inside of locker doors or have become too dog eared for further use. In most ships these books just appeared in twos and threes, but with Albert in the crew there was a seemingly inexhaustible supply, selected moreover from amongst those which catered to the latest fashion, for fashions there most certainly were. Some years the subjects were fully clothed in sweaters, shoes and stockings, but had for some unexplained reason completely mislaid every item of clothing except suspender belts from thigh to navel. Other years these same ladies had managed to retain undergarments whose brevity was matched only by their transparency; sometimes the favourites were facing their audience, at others they would have the other cheek turned to the camera lens. There was a racist bias too, not in skin colour but in detail revealed. Those models photographed in the UK and commonwealth could be naked but had to have their more private parts tastefully and carefully painted out, thus presenting a seamless perfection from front to rear. If photographed in Scandinavia any effort to conceal even the densest of pubic hair or what nestled beneath was taboo. The American versions displayed unlikely combinations of erotically seductive poses with the fullest possible naked exposure down to the waist but an almost complete cover up of any evidence of sexuality below the navel. Nookie could identify the year and country of origin of most pictures from these and other idiosyncrasies, and he always kept for his cronies delectation a well thumbed collection of the best and most fashionable.

With all this extra-curricular activity Albert's work as Second Cook might have appeared as a sideline, but not so for it was vital to the crew's well-being. Once clear of port fresh bread was needed daily, and every afternoon the distinctive baking smell pervaded the ship. Only someone familiar with the sea would have identified it as such, for it was not the warm floury odour of new shore side bread, but the distinctive aroma created by the scorched grease proof paper lining the baking tins. Somehow shipboard bread has neither the softness of the store baked variety, nor the delicious crusts of the home baked; but then it has never been necessary to coax sailors' appetites, quantity not quality being the essential requirement. Besides this baking Albert's task was to work alongside the Chief Cook, for feeding around fifty men is not a single handed job. The two men also had the assistance of a Galley Boy, who spent virtually all his working life peeling potatoes, scouring pots and scrubbing down the galley, all tasks which were beneath the dignity of the qualified men. Not perhaps the most exciting of jobs, but young Harry had hopes of promotion into Albert's berth in the next trip or so. This was probably within his grasp, but his secret ambition to emulate the Second Cook's sexual role, was not. The Galley Boy would perhaps achieve a moderate degree of success, but in the same way that neither environment nor upbringing can ever quite confer the initial advantages of the old school tie, so in her chosen way had Maggie benefitted Albert Costino so many years before.

Albert's shore activities might have destined him to a lonely existence in middle age, with no real home between trips, but for the past few years Albert had rushed for the train rather than stay to drink with his shipmates on Pay-Off Day. At Glasgow Central he raced down the platform into the arms of a diminutive, excited female figure, elegantly wrapped, but barely able to conceal her promise of an even more exciting unwrapping. Mrs. Costello, for they were legally wed, had come from the same close tenement community, she knew its rules and she knew her Albert. She was supremely confident of her man, just so long as she had him mind, body, and hands for herself; a confidence resulting from experience backed by advice given over the years since adolescence by her favourite aunt, Maggie.

Chapter 12

**David Farnell,
Fifth Engineer**

The Fiver[1] was a good man to have on a run ashore; he did not dance, but should any of the rest of us pick up a girl and ferry her over to David's corner we knew she would be 'safe' for the rest of the evening. This was because David had a silver tongued way with women, a most valuable asset when we had only a very few evenings in which to make and hold social contacts in the face of opposition from all the other ships in port. Without David, lasting success until sailing day would have been nearly impossible.

His talent was one he held in common with many of his Welsh compatriots. Although the distinctive national culture had played little part in his education or his home life, it nevertheless must have lain dormant awaiting a suitable opportunity for its exercise. That it should have materialised as a fluency in small talk, sufficient to hold girls on a dance floor, was perhaps unexpected - but it was certainly to our advantage. The drill was for the Third mate to collect one by one those selected for our group, for not only was he good looking, he was a very good dancer as well. He would ferry them over to us, and David would start the chat going whilst the rest of us provided a service to and from the bar or circled the floor inexpertly with any of the girls who were showing signs of restlessness. We had all sailed together for some time and worked well as a team afloat and particularly ashore, where David's marshalling of our forays it was quite impressive, especially if the rig was 'blues'[2]. It was unusual to see a tramp ship officer ashore in uniform, comparatively few had one respectable enough to be seen off the ship, and our group must have been virtually unique. The girls were not unappreciative. They were there to be picked up and the smoothness of our operation must have flattered them. It also hinted that the inevitable aftermath might be better than the standard foreplay of 'Drinks before or after?' of most shipboard parties - although the end result would hopefully be the same.

1. Fiver - *Fifth Engineer, responsible for deck machinery*
2. Blues - *Double breasted, brass buttoned naval uniform*

The reason that David did not dance was attributable to his Welsh background. He had served his apprenticeship in a Cardiff shipyard where it was the whimps who went out with girls, while the real men played rugby and drank beer. His years as a scrum half had given him a real thirst, a quite substantial beer drinker's belly and a slight limp, this last a legacy from a friendly match and sixteen stone of Llanelli full back. So David had to leave all but the slowest dancing to us while he conversed alongside the bar, the pivot of our campaign to prevent our newly acquired flock from being cut out by other marauding ships' crews.

Despite his limp David was far from inactive. He was a fresh air fiend and something of a fitness fanatic, neither of which seemed to match his ample girth, but that is life. A love of fresh air was possibly unusual in a ship's engineer who had deliberately chosen a working life below decks amongst steam and thrashing pistons; however David had not yet fully taken up that subterranean life. His only routine engine duties were assisting with the engine manoeuvres whilst entering or leaving port, for shutting off steam to the main engines and clutching them in to go astern was a physically arduous task calling for at least two qualified men. Normally the watches were kept by the Second, Third and Fourth Engineers, whilst the Fifth Engineer worked on deck where the machinery was his specific charge. There was not a great deal of it; two winches at each of the five hatches, the windlass for'ard and the steering engine aft, but it was old and just to keep it in running order took up all the available working time between ports. So most days David could be found working on the winches or at his bench in the lee of the after deck house. You could always tell where he was by the clump of his hammer, or by his dungaree clad legs protruding from under a winch bed or by his loud tuneless singing - one thing he had certainly not inherited from his Welsh ancestry was any form of musical talent.

His enjoyment of fresh air he took lightly, but his fitness was a deadly serious matter. He had found out early on that beer without exercise was the shortest route to excess weight and a falling off of his bedroom prowess. So rather than cut down his drinking he had instituted a daily exercise routine, carried out come hell or high water. It was based on that commercially available to any seven stone weakling tired of having sand kicked in his face and consisted of pitting the strength of the muscles of one limb against those of the other, unfortunately while building up impressive muscle it did little to reduce a beer gut, but the exercises were well suited to the limited space of the Fifth Engineer's cabin, about ten feet square at the most. They also provided a definite psychological advantage; most of the crew were accidentally fit by virtue of the life they led, only David had the inner satisfaction of believing his physical well being was due to his own efforts.

As David was the centre of our group ashore so he was on board. This was as much due to availability as personality, for whilst watches kept the ship to a twenty four working day its crew still clung to a nine to five routine for leisure, and it was only in the evenings that we felt the inclination to sit around and talk. As there was no recreational space on board we had to use a cabin. It could not be that of the graveyard watchkeepers who needed to slide off to bed soon after seven, nor the Third Mate's or Fourth Engineer's as they had to go on watch at eight, nor Sparks or the Apprentices whose cabins were too close to the Captain's, nor the two other watchkeepers who were on watch until eight. That left only David's cabin, so it was here that we foregathered most evenings. Our discussions covered a surprisingly wide field. Abstract ideas, especially morals and religion were popular topics as we all fancied ourselves as modern emancipated thinkers. Although David appeared to lead I am certain that he listened as much as, or possibly more than he spoke; but even so his ideas came across with great clarity and conviction. They were not the typical mores of the middle class community from which he had come, but a highly personalised blend of ideologies, being both anti-establishment and anti-dogmatic at the same time. In his travel around the world he had, like the rest of us, observed life under a range of political conditions from the racialist supremacy of White Africa to the militaristic regimes of both Fascist and Communist. Most of us accepted this as something that need have little direct impact on our own British way of life, after all we were not many years short of MacMillan's 'Never had it so good' generation, but David felt unease and contempt in equal degrees for the masters of all non-egalitarian systems.

David had a vivid manner of bringing home his points, for conversation was to him a most vital facet of life. As time passed it assumed an even greater importance, as did an antipathy to the sweltering working conditions below decks. At thirty he decided enough was enough and took stock of his position. The outcome was to be of moment to circles far removed from his cabin on board a tramp steamer; as a Trade Union official he is now a familiar and friendly, if somewhat argumentative television personality to a far wider audience.

Chapter 13

**Tommy Farragher,
Very Nearly a Greaser**

Well he had made it and was quietly celebrating. Tommy Farragher, late private Lancashire Fusileers (twenty years), Merchant Navy Fireman Trimmer (ten years) was now rated Greaser, his only real promotion in thirty years since leaving school in Birkenhead. Admittedly he had made Lance Corporal on more than one occasion; the first time he had held his stripe for a mere half day, returning joyously to barracks after wetting it, he had fallen foul of the MP on the gate. The next time he had held the stripe longer, but was lucky to have escaped the glasshouse when it was lost as the result of a free for all in an Aldershot pub. The army did not give him a third chance. So Tommy had entered World War II with the same rank with which he celebrated VE Day, as a Private. He had fought across North Africa and up through Italy with a fair degree of efficiency, fighting was the one thing he was good at, but without any outstanding merit, no awards, no Good Conduct Medal, just a full set of campaign ribbons. After the war things were dull for an old sweat around barracks full of National Servicemen still wet behind the ears and boredom as much as anything else kept Tommy in and out of trouble until, eventually, his time up, the army were only too delighted to discharge him.

He was a typical ex-soldier, ramrod straight, tattooed arms and torso, military moustache, the lot. He joined the Merchant Navy as a stoker and quickly lost the upright stance, shuffling about with the same gait as everyone else who wheelbarrowed coal around the bunkers for a living; a duck-like walk, flat footed with toes turned out and a nautical roll to boot. The moustache went next after a first long trip in the tropics, the mixture of coal dust and sweat running down his upper lip into his mouth every time he opened it was an overriding argument for becoming clean shaven. The uniform changed too; the years of khaki fatigues were replace by old dungarees, a grimy singlet and an even grimier sweat rag tied round his neck. The only sign of individuality was his steaming revvy. It was no different in material, the standard blue denim; nor in form, as shapeless as everyone else's; nor in cleanliness, coal be-grimed like the rest; but it did sport a regimental cap badge and was always worn at an angle rakish enough to have given any sergeant major apoplexy. His task as a Fireman Trimmer was to keep the pockets topped up for his mates on the stokehold floor. You could often hear his complaints about the 'Focking Pockets' delivered in broad Scouse, but perhaps he was entitled to grumble as the ship burned about thirty-six tons of coal a day and he had to shift twelve tons of this in his two four hour watches, shovelling every last knob into a wheelbarrow, trundling it along the side bunker and emptying it into the pocket. It was however seaman's grumbling; so long as it could be heard then there was little wrong on board, only if it went silent was there likely to be any trouble.

After shovelling his way across the oceans of the world for ten years, and actually keeping out of trouble for the last five of them, he had made Greaser. No more hurling coal into the maw of the boilers day in, day out. His watches would now be kept in the engine room alongside the watchkeeping engineers. He would have to keep the various moving parts topped up with lubricants, including a once per watch patrol of the shaft tunnel running aft under number four and five holds, ensuring that each bearing was running sweetly and not overheating. The principal change would be from the stifling heat of the stokehold to the strident noise of the main engine and the screeching whine of the auxiliary machinery; in the one case you were cooked, in the other deafened. It was a toss up which made the watch pass faster; either way you wished your life away from port to port.

Some ports were better than others, but all had their drawbacks. For example in Rio you could barely afford to drink but the bars were open all night; in Australia you could afford to drink but the bars closed promptly at six. In retrospect most ports were better in anticipation than reality, none matched up to the 'good old army canteens' that Tommy had given up for the more exciting prospect of life at sea. He would have been disillusioned had he been a thinking man, but as an old sweat he was prone to neither illusions nor deep thinking just so long as he had a pint pot in his hand. Like many others on board Tommy had no real life, just an existence; no hobbies, just off-watch smoking and sleeping (tramp ships were dry); no real ambition except to find a cushier billet. Now with promotion to Greaser he had found that billet. It was not more exciting than before, but it was better paid. Better pay meant more cash to drink ashore; more shore drinking would make life on board take longer to catch up with Tommy's deep seated ennui; more than that he did not expect from life.

"Time, Gentlemen, Please." Tommy did not budge, his pint pot was still half full. "Come on, lads, drink up." this time more aggressively from the barman, but Tommy's pot was still not empty. Eventually it was removed by the barman along with the overflowing ashtrays and crumpled crisp packets. Tommy felt cheated and but was not spoiling for a fight, he knew the barman and wanted to drink here again, and anyway as a Greaser he was above unprovoked pub brawling. He rose and left.

Outside it was dark and Tommy did not notice the figure in blue, but he did have an urgent need to relieve himself and the wall was the most suitable place to hand. The Constable was not amused, especially as his uniform was accidentally sprayed as he moved in for the kill. Tommy woke up next morning in a cell. This was nothing unusual, it had happened many times before. His overnight sojourn had caused him to miss the ship which had sailed without him, but this had happened before as well. It meant that he could forget his new found rate of Greaser, but he had lost stripes before and in a far better outfit than the Merchant Navy. Tommy closed his eyes and settled down again to wait for his shake, accompanied by its inevitable mug of lousy police station tea.

Chapter 14

**John Angel Wills,
Second Steward**

Readers of sea stories are made only too well aware that there were homosexuals among the catering staff of passenger liners. They did exist but probably were far more numerous in fiction than in reality. On tramp ships they were a rarity indeed for there was little to attract them to the absolute grime and comparative squalor of a coal burning cargo carrier. John Angel Wills was one such rarity; a fastidiously clean, gentle soul to whom the roughness of a tramp ship must have been a sore trial on many an occasion. It was indeed difficult to understand why he signed on trip after trip, but over the years he had become one of the ship's few fixtures.

Although appropriate, Angel was not a nickname, he had been christened with his mother's maiden name some twenty five years previously and now invariably chirped 'Johnny Angel' when asked his given name. Ashore he would have passed unnoticed as a rather willowy young man. It was only in the coarser closed society of a tramp ship that he stood apart. He was not a practising gay at sea, being far too gentle to be attracted by the overtures made by the hard cases on board. In fact, surprisingly, his gentleness had become generally respected and he was left virtually unmolested on board after the first few days of each new trip.

As Second Steward he was nominally the number two of the catering staff and was supposed to deputise for the Chief Steward in the latter's absence, but this role had no appeal for Johnny, he avoided it whenever possible and preferred to leave any delegated authority to the Chief Cook. The other part of his duty was to act as the Captain's Steward, assisting in the pantry when the Captain ate in the saloon, or providing a private service when he did not. In the very worst weather the only thing that stood between the ship and disaster was the Captain and his ability to remain alert for days on end with only snatched seconds of sleep in the chartroom. At these times Johnny's slight figure was constantly hovering about the open bridge with the hot drinks and snack meals which alone enabled the captain to remain on his feet. Then at the height of the gale you might observe to the full an alternative, literal, dimension to the poetic truth of Milton's deathless line 'They also serve.....'

Johnny's special pride was the Captain's cabin. Strictly speaking it was more than just a cabin, it was the only suite on board, for even the Chief Engineer did not rate a bathroom of his own. The furnishings were not very grand, but under Johnny's loving care every piece of brightwork gleamed and the patina on the cheap veneered plywood fittings rivalled that of any stately home. This was a marked contrast to the steel walled cabin with iron framed bunks and green painted metal lockers that Johnny shared with the Assistant Steward. It was one of his greatest moments when he was complimented on the condition of the captain's cabin and one of his greatest regrets that it was not on the route of the Captain's Sunday morning inspection and so did not receive a regular weekly commendation. Just a few words of praise and Johnny would have blushed to the roots of his wispy bottle blond hair, whistling contentedly as he busied himself about the remainder of that particular day's chores.

Whistling was one of his trademarks, pop music his great love, and given other opportunities he might have been something in the music profession. As it was he had a complete repertoire of every hit song for the last ten years and as he worked he made music; whistling out loud for pleasure; humming whenever he was working close enough to bother those around him; and singing in a very passable baritone when he thought he was out of everyone's earshot. His most prized possession was a radio, an Eddystone 720, very much more expensive than those usually found on board, and from 1300 to 1500, the traditional steward's lunch break, Johnny would tune into any music he could find on short wave. He had to listen on earphones as his cabin mate invariably got his head down in the rest period, so every afternoon you could find Johnny sitting silently, nodding his head smilingly in time to the latest dance rhythms of his own private world.

At sea Johnny was happily at peace. His sexual peculiarity was overlooked and he was an individual in his own right. Ashore he had to come into contact with the outside world, and so became to some extent a lost soul cut off from his fellow men. A tramp ship is no place to stay in port. At sea it is bearable for there is a certain degree of restfulness to be derived from the steady thump of the engines, from the daily routine and from the limitless expanse of water that forms the backdrop. In port engine noises are replaced by the irregular crash of cargo gear; routine is replaced by the chaotic exigencies of discharge and reloading; and the view is limited by the blank ugly faces of warehouses. Fortunately for Johnny most ports provided a refuge in their Seamen's Missions, with Catholic, Established and Non-Conformist Churches vieing with each other to minister to the wandering seafarer. These missions tended to be adult versions of youth clubs with dance floor, table tennis, billiard table and coffee bar, their only entrance fee a gentle persuasion to attend a religious epilogue prior to closing for the night. They only filled up when the crew was broke, or on Sundays if the pubs and cinemas remained shut; but you could always count on a handful of habitues and amongst them Johnny. The kindly interest of the Missioners and the comfort of the armchairs were the best shoreside attractions he had found. In return Johnny was always among the few who attended the epilogue, not because he was religious but because he was too gentle to wish to offer the slightest offence to his hosts.

Gentleness was probably Johnny's overriding characteristic. It was always Johnny who made himself responsible for the ship's cat if it was sick or had kittens. It was always Johnny who from somewhere produced the coloured decorations at Christmas. When one of the Firemen was sent ashore with a broken leg it was Johnny who organised a 'Get Well' card, no one else would have even spared it a thought. In any other environment these acts might have gained him much greater regard than the tolerance which was so hard won at sea, but that was just Johnny's lot.

The highlight of his voyage came on Pay-Off day. The crew, lined up in their shore going best, faced the Captain over the Shipping Office counter ready to receive their pay, invariably in cash as almost none had either a bank account or savings. Some were asked to sign on again, most were content to take their money and go, symptomatic of the transient relationship between a tramp ship and her crew. But always when Johnny came to the desk it was the same. "Thank you, Wills. I hope to see you back with us next trip." The Captain would push the new articles across for Johnny to sign, and blushing to the roots of his newly trimmed hair he would carefully inscribe his signature on the appropriate line, then whistling the latest hit tune he would march happily out into the grimy dockside morning.

Chapter 15

Jack and Wally,
Able Seamen

Jack and Wally were inseparable. For years they had sailed together, keeping the same watches. Even between voyages they were next door neighbours on an Avonmouth council estate. Yet they were an oddly assorted pair, Wally's six and a half feet well overtopping Jack's five foot nothing. Wally was taciturn whilst Jack's rich West Country burr could always be used to locate the two ABs. There was a great discrepancy in their ages too; Wally was in early middle age, Jack looked barely out of his teens. Thus it was no surprise that Wally sometimes said to Jack, "Look, I've been doing it this way since before you were born." This was a nearly true statement for the two had sailed together since Jack's first trip as a Deck Boy.

Both were modern seamen, highly skilled at sugeeing, painting, chipping and the thousand and one tasks connected with the running of a steel steamship. Yet although both were successors to the West Countrymen who sailed with Drake and Hawkins, the seamens' tasks on a sailing ship would have been completely foreign to them. On a modern ship the skills they required were more closely akin to those of a shore side building worker than to those of their sailormen ancestors. On deck the two of them worked as a team and so the Bosun invariably called on them for the double handed tasks. For example it was always Jack and Wally who 'did' the stays. The four and a half inch standing rigging was painted every other trip with a mixture half white lead paint, half tallow. A paste this thick would have defied any paint brush, so a much simpler technique was used. A bosun's chair was rigged at the cross trees and Jack with an old sack over his shoulders was pulled up the stay. On reaching the top Jack dipped a lump of cotton waste in his paint pot and then gripped it firmly around the stay as Wally lowered him slowly back to deck level. By the time the job was completed you could barely recognise Jack under his coating of white lead and tallow, and Wally was liberally bedaubed as well. However this did not worry them; the stays were always a Saturday 'job and finish' and as they could be completed in a forenoon it gave the pair of them an extra half day off. They would use this free time seated in the mess room, Jack talking on and on, Wally answering with the occasional monosyllable whilst puffing out huge clouds of smoke from the pipe that rarely left his mouth. Jack never smoked, perhaps he had always been too busy talking. This was fortunate because in port it took both of their duty free allowances to keep Wally's pipe going, even at a reduced rate. Another job not too popular with most sailors was painting the side. The paint was the poorest quality used and working over the side was a sure way of getting covered in the stuff. But for Jack and Wally it was another chance of working together. The painting stages were simple planks suspended on ropes that required one man at each end to operate them. So too compensate for the minor inconveniences of the job they could spend the whole day chatting as they worked; or rather Jack chattered whilst Wally grunted occasionally in reply. In fact the two of them were always happier on these and the other dirtier jobs, such as cleaning holds or scraping winch beds. This was because supervision was relaxed and provided they got on with the job the Bosun kept off their backs, turning a blind eye to the inevitable plume of smoke from Wally's pipe, for officially smoking was not permitted during working hours. For Jack these jobs might have an extra bonus; if they were exceptionally dirty and arduous the Mate had been known to give the boys a tot afterwards and as Wally rarely, if ever, drank it might mean a double tot for Jack. He was also able to double up again when the crew were issued with their weekly tot. Although it was strictly against the rules the Chief Steward had known them long enough to give both tots to one man.

As both were married men they preferred quiet runs ashore and had become film addicts. They now rated a port by the number of different pictures showing at any one time, and a voyage's success by the number of ports with decent cinemas. Their film going was a seven day a week affair, often with two shows on Saturday and Sunday. The pattern of these runs ashore rarely changed. After work they washed and put on their shore going clothes, the older man always with a tweed jacket surmounting his dungarees, the younger with a red checked shirt and a wind cheater. Their only concessions to this rule were that in the tropics they might leave their jackets off and in colder climes they would both don duffel coats. They would march down the gangway promptly at 1800 heading for the nearest bar. Here Wally would get his pipe really stoked up whilst Jack would down three or four pints in quick succession, talking the while. Sometimes Wally would have a single half pint, and on very rare occasions he had been known to answer Jack with a complete sentence, but mostly he just sat and smoked. This regular session always ended in sufficient time for them to be seated when the curtain went up for the last house. One of the major crosses that Wally had to bear was the 'No Smoking' laws of Australia and New Zealand. In the interval he was always the first in the rush to the lobby to snatch a few puffs before the main feature. After the show they would stroll back to the ship, Jack animatedly discoursing on the film they had seen, Wally as ever amicably grunting in reply. Always they were back on board before eleven, well before the rest of the crowd who tended to remain ashore until the bars closed or their money ran out. If the ship should happen to be in a port with no cinemas then either Jack or Wally would volunteer for the nightwatchman's duty, and whichever one it was the other would sit with him in the galley until well into the early hours, the one talking, the other wreathed in blue clouds of his favourite St.Bruno.

For these two it was a contented well ordered life. I sailed with them for some time, but never saw them in any kind of trouble. Nor can I ever remember ever seeing the one without the other. The pall of tobacco smoke surrounding Wally and the rich burr of Jack's voice were indivisible and whilst being friendly towards the rest of us they rarely invited us to join in their conversation. Co-incidentally Jack was short for Jonathan and Wally's surname was Saul and there was something classic in the friendship of these two men. To paraphrase the Second Book of Samuel, 'Saul and Jonathan were lovely and pleasant in their lives'.

Their last trip together was on the Lode Star out of Liverpool with steel rails for Rio. She was lost at sea with all hands when her cargo shifted in a mid-winter Atlantic gale in 1952.

Chapter 16

John Garson,
Marine Superintendent

The man in the trilby shivered and drew his overcoat more tightly around his thin shoulders. There was not much wind, but the air coming off the river was chill and damp. Around him there were lights, dim yellowish pools in the gloom, each one illuminating a hatchway or a gangway, but in front of him, as yet, nothing but empty bollards and the oily blackness of the water lapping against the vacant berth. He was not alone, sheltering in the shadow of the warehouse were the longshoremen waiting to take the mooring ropes, their presence indicated by sporadic low bursts of talking and the occasional glow of a dog end not fully shielded by a cupped hand - for officially smoking was not permitted on the dockside. The Ship's Agent was also there standing respectfully a few paces to the rear, ready to offer polite conversation, but the hunched figure was not in a talkative mood. For one thing he was cold, for another his mind was fully occupied with the papers locked in the brief case at his feet.

Among these his principal concern was the defect list radioed ahead by the Master, for the man beneath the trilby hat was John Garson, Marine Superintendent of the Farron Steamshipping Company, owners of a six ship strong tramp fleet. Rectifying their defects was John Garson's prime responsibility. The incoming ship, the Sironia was, like all the Farron Line, rather elderly, so her list of minor ailments was a long one. Many were familiar, for example the windlass gave trouble trip after trip and always featured in the Chief Engineer's report. Invariably after wasting time and money on it nothing was found to be wrong; yet with equal regularity it would once again play up as soon as the ship left home waters. There were some newcomers as well, sure signs of increasing age; winch beds rusting through, auxiliary machinery needing replacement, which latter could perhaps be put off until the next drydocking, but could not be ignored for too long. Included in the list, as in any other, would be items reflecting the 'betes noire' of the Chief Engineer. With Mr. Holding of the Sironia there was always a fair number of defects in the fresh water feed system. With Bob Thompson of the Tyronia it would have been deck winches. All these would be the subject of a Dutch Auction between the Chief and the Super. The former would agree to defer some of the minor defects caused by age, the Super would allow some of the Chiefs modifications to the fresh water feed, the overall list would traditionally be reduced by around ten percent to satisfy the owners, and the ship would go to sea again in a reasonable enough state of seaworthiness.

It was now 3 a.m. and there was still no sign of the ship, but she must be locking in as the Berthing Master pedalled past on his bicycle and the Customs Officers had drawn up in their van. John Garson shivered again; at his age standing on a cold dock in midwinter was not a favourite pastime; it had more than once given him a chill that had put him in bed for weeks. However it was part of his job to be there, a sort of public relations exercise by Head Office, for there was little real work he could do in the few hours remaining before daylight. But for both Master and Chief Engineer it would be an affront not to be greeted by the Marine Superintendent no matter what hour of the day or night they docked.

They thought he had it easy, or rather John had thought his own Marine Superintendents had had it easy when he was a junior sea going engineer, although by the time he rose to the rank of Chief he had some inkling of the trials and tribulations of fleet management. It was not the work, which was hard though satisfying, and he certainly could not complain about the salary, but with half a dozen ships there was almost always one in port requiring his near constant presence. Sometimes he did not see his London office for weeks on end, and as for his wife and family, he often thought that perhaps he might have seen more of them when he was at sea. On top of this he did not, unlike the sea staff, have a cabin in which to make some semblance of a home whilst he was away. He had to live on trains from London to outlying destinations, and out of a suitcase in a series of hotels. The delights of even the best in North East coast ports very soon palled. They came basically in two types, the old and grimy with dark panelling, aged plush, no clientele to speak of and very inefficient heating, or the new with chrome, plastic, and a regular drinking school drawn from the local business community noisily seated around the cocktail bar. John was not really fond of either.

It was now three thirty, and at last the darkness in front of him was broken by slowly moving shapes dimly outlined by the clusters[1] now being rigged in the alleyways and gangways. Not before time, he thought, stamping his cold deadened feet and, hunching even more deeply into his overcoat, he picked up his briefcase. "Good Morning, Mr. Garson. the Captain's waiting for you in his cabin." The Third Mate paused briefly to make this observation to the Super, but made no offer of an

---

1. Cluster - *Large portable lighting on a long lead used for temporary illumination of deck and holds*

escort. Both were well aware that the Third had work still awaiting him, and that the older man knew exactly where to go.

"Good Morning, Captain. Have a good trip?" "Good Morning, Mr. Garson. Whisky?" Both were formal well worn greetings, rhetorical questions delivered almost simultaneously, with no answers needed or expected on either side. The evidence of the goodness or otherwise of the trip was carefully detailed in the Voyage Report neatly folded and ready on the desk, although it contained little of moment that had not been telegraphed well ahead to the London Office. The Super's grateful acceptance of a warming tot after a long wait was more than obvious from the humanising effect it had on his cold pinched features.

"The Chief will be along as soon as he has washed up." continued the Captain; again another of the carefully preserved formalities, a brief time for the Captain to pass on any information to which the Chief Engineer ought not to be privy. As usual there was none. At this hour of the morning there was little point in getting down to the ship's business, but the drink in the warm informality of the cabin was a necessary function to demonstrate the privileged position of the ship's two senior officers. Later the Mate would look in to report the ship secured alongside, to ascertain when and how many gangs were ordered for cargo work, to accept a drink and then depart for what was left of his night's sleep. The Chief Steward would also look in, to ascertain if the Captain and the Super had everything they required. He might be offered a drink, but this would depend on how long he had been in the Company's employ; old Sam Herbert had been with Farrons for over thirty years and would mortally be offended if he did not get such an invitation.

After all these worthies had come and gone the Captain, the Chief and the Super would spend a further hour or so in casual talk, although shop would predominate. Then, the niceties observed, the Super would go ashore. On this occasion he knew he would have little sleep before facing a gelid hotel breakfast, but pressed and cleanly shaven he would have to be back on board by 0930 to begin work in earnest.

It would be a busy fortnight, the crew had to be paid off, a load of timber discharged, bunkers and stores replenished before the ship sailed in ballast for London. In between these activities the Super and the Chief Engineer had to plan the various repair jobs and a boiler clean. This meant that he would have to sail round the coast in order to finish his work onboard, which would mean a third week away from the office. Still as he lived near London he might be able to sleep at home. He might even get a weekend with his wife, that is provided the Tyronia did not put in at Rotterdam. It was still a toss up whether the charterers would want the next vessel there at the weekend or midweek in London. If the former it would be at least five weeks before he saw home or office again.

Yes, he reflected, yawning over his final drink, maybe there was something to say for the comparatively stable life of a sea-going Engineer after all.

Chapter 17

Shack,
Feles Navalis

Shack stalked the decks in the strikingly handsome coat that had caused him to be named after Len Shackleton, star of Newcastle United. None of that team's black and white shirts were laundered so often, nor gleamed so brightly as Shack's coat. This was because of the countless hours spent cleaning it. Shack had time for that, for he alone of all on board had no official duties whatsoever, for Shack was the Ship's Cat.

Landsmen might think that the purpose of carrying a cat would be to keep down rats, but a single glance at Shack's smooth gleaming fur and rotund flanks confirmed that here, at any rate was one cat with no need to hunt for his supper. The same is true of every other modern ship's cat for with little of a normal domestic life ships' companies lavish attention on their cats. Shack had only to appear at the galley door or in any of the mess rooms to be inundated with offers of food and milk.

Unlike the rest of the crew, whose normal stay on board was one trip, perhaps two or three at most, the ship was Shack's permanent home. He had even been born on board, abaft the funnel, under the canvas cover of Number Three Lifeboat. This made him even more a part of the ship than most cats who first come up the gangway as tiny furred bundles hidden under a seaman's shirt.

Shack had no specific role on board, for even had he been so inclined there were few rats around waiting to be caught. He had however taken on certain duties for himself. For example he would follow the Captain's procession on Sunday morning inspections, but only within the limits of the particular section of accommodation in which he happened to be at the time, never out across the deck towards the next. He was also in attendance whenever the pilot ladder was being rigged by Number Three Hatch, although apart from a cursory welcoming sniff he showed little or no further interest in the pilot. Saturday night at sea Shack was always present in the Chief Steward's cabin to supervise the crew's weekly tot and their purchase of cigarettes. In none of these activities was there an obvious cat like motive; Shack was there and that was all there was to it.

Apart from these self imposed duties, sleeping was his major daylight occupation, and within reason he would sleep wherever and whenever he fancied. If the weather was warm and dry Shack's black and white form could be seen sunning itself on one of the after hatches, or if it was really hot under a lifeboat in what little shade it provided. If the weather was wet, cold or stormy he could be in any of several places; the sailors' mess room, the Bosun's settee, Chippy's shop or for some inexplicable feline reason curled up in the yellow painted biscuit tin that served the Second Mate as a waste paper basket. There were of course certain places that were out of bounds, notably the galley and the Captain's cabin. These he avoided with the disdainful punctiliousness of his race. No one was ever quite sure where Shack spent his nights, but you could not stand around the deck for more than a couple of minutes before a purring shadow detached itself from the surrounding darkness to wrap itself companionably about your ankles. What he was doing, how he heard your movement or sensed your need for fellowship was another of the unknowable processes of his mind. Whatever it was, a night time stroll would not have been the same without Shack's furry presence.

In common with all ships' cats Shack went ashore in port and was rarely seen on board until sailing. From this has grown the popular myth that credits a ship's cat with a mystic sixth sense that responds to a ship's intention to sail. This is not so, and for a perfectly logical reason. When cargo is being worked a tramp ship's deck with steam pipes cracking and hissing everywhere is certainly no place to sleep in the sun by day, and by night the feline population of dockside warehouses make them far more congenial places than any ship. However every night, almost as soon as the winches stopped clattering and the hatches were covered, Shack's black and white form would steal up the gangway to prowl around his domain, filling himself with whatever he could find before returning to the wharf to complete his nocturnal activities. As most of the crew were by then ashore they were unaware of his nightly visits, and so to account for his re-appearance on sailing day they were prepared to allow the cats a prescience they do not possess. Sometimes cats do not rejoin their ships. Quite often a daytime sailing leaves behind a furry form contentedly sunning itself on a warehouse floor, inevitably to be replaced by a kitten off the dockside at the next port of call.

This was not to be Shack's fate, already his days were numbered, but he was not destined to be left on some foreign shore, nor to grow old and dirty as the continual battle against shipboard grime became too much of an effort. He was, sadly, to be a victim of his own regular habits.

The reason cats were no longer needed to keep down shipboard rats was the regular fumigation carried out under Board of Trade Regulations. All the crew were sent to hotels overnight, the ship was sealed off, red skull and crossbones notices were then plastered everywhere and all the enclosed spaces flushed through with potassium cyanide gas. The following day after a thorough examination the vessel would be declared gas free and the few dead rats removed. 'Gas Free' was in practice a comparative term. Quite definitely there were not enough traces of the gas left to endanger life, but soft furnishings retained a distinctive unpleasant smell for days, and anyone unwise enough to leave a pipe in his cabin would find it had become so impregnated as to make it completely unsmokable ever after. This was Shack's undoing. Usually, despite his most vociferous protests, he would be securely nailed up in a crate and left at the dockyard gate by the hotel bound crew. On this one occasion he could not be found on board, nor later could he read the warning notices as he approached for his accustomed nightly visit. The end was mercifully short, the gas taking effect before Shack even reached the deck. The following day he was found stiff and cold only half way up the gangway. The irony was that to his corpse the Port Health Officer was able to add only five rather undernourished rats, for since her last fumigation the ship had carried nothing but completely inedible cargoes of coal, iron ore and phosphate. The final ignominy was that a barely weaned tabby replacement was spirited aboard the very same afternoon and directly found its way to the Bosun's settee.

Chapter 18

**George Fingal,
Chief Engineer**

'Here we go again' the junior apprentice groaned to himself inwardly. This was a standard reaction to Mr. Fingal's opening conversational gambit, "Now on the old Homerian......" The whole saloon had heard it before, many times. The Homerian and the Olympian had been sister ships cruising for the old Silver Star Line. Mr. Fingal had served on them both in his youth and they had furnished him with conversation ever since. It had been the heyday of the ocean liner, and Mr. Fingal, an inveterate name dropper, never tired of repeating his accounts of the near famous of thirty years earlier who had been passengers on them. There was, for example, Althen Simpson-Watts, tennis star of a Wimbledon when long dresses had graced the Centre Court. "She was quite a girl." he would conclude. Then there was Lady Cynthia Shellman-Peters married at various times to a baronet, a newspaper tycoon and several assorted film stars. She too had been "Quite a girl." There were many others, all were given this same accolade. Mr. Fingal never explained himself, it was one of those 'things' between men: by inference it gave the Chief Engineer the reputation of a ladies' man, but whether justified or not remained a secret between Mr. Fingal and the ladies themselves.

There were also the ladies' male counterparts, the financiers, captains of industry and others who travelled on the cruise liners. Mr. Fingal's stories of these had two basic plots. There were those where business opportunities were revealed to Mr. Fingal, which for some reason or another he had not followed up, and there were those that showed that these famous folk were really 'one of the boys' at heart, and liked nothing better than to demonstrate in Mr. Fingal's company that the crasser human appetites recognise no barriers of class or wealth.

As a junior engineer Mr. Fingal had sailed on these ships for many years and doubtless some of the stories must have been true, for he was still a handsome figure of a man, with a crop of iron grey hair and an air of rough competence that still made women look twice. Nor was he unaware of this. His apparently casual hair style took quite some while to adjust - something unknown to everyone on board except the Engineer's Steward who cleaned the chief's cabin. The steward was also the only person to suspect that the virile greyness of Mr. Fingal's hair was not entirely attributable to natural sources. Mr. Fingal's clothes were immaculate too, but rather surprisingly they were somewhat dated. On board he affected a blue patrol jacket, buttoned up to the neck like a guardsman's tunic, four purple edged gold stripes gleaming from its shoulder boards, a form of dress rarely seen in the Merchant Navy even before the Second World War. Mr. Fingal's must have been about the only one to have survived into the post war era. His shore going clothes were the same; good quality, impeccable cut, but quite inescapably modelled on the English country gentlemen of the nineteen-thirties.

His speech was almost exactly what you would expect, a deep masculine voice, as befitted his build, but with a carefully over aspirated use of words, reminiscent of a music hall cockney doing a 'posh' turn. Whenever he spoke his choice of words gave an impression of dated self-importance. Perhaps it had started as a guise but it had been habit to Mr. Fingal for so long that now it came naturally. He was always Mr. Fingal, too. Obviously he had a christian name, it was George, but no one ever heard it used on board. Many suspected that even his wife referred to him in bed by the same 'Mr. Fingal' she used in public.

On the Homerian there had been many ways of passing the time, people milling around the bars and lounges, entertainments on deck, and even on watch there had been at least three engineers with broadly similar tasks and seniority. Here, on a tramp ship there were no passengers, no entertainments and only one engineer to each watch. As Chief Engineer he was also, by tradition, the confidant of the Captain and so could not be on too close terms with anyone else on board. This had inevitably made him turn inwards for relaxation, and as reading had for him little appeal he tried various handicrafts which were mere time fillers until he discovered oils. Now in his spare time he was a painter of some skill and great industry, with a style and range of subject matter peculiarly dictated by his tastes and the shipboard environment.

Most artists in his circumstances would have produced ships, seascapes and other nauticalia, but not Mr. Fingal. He preferred landscapes, so he produced them - hills, mountains, woodland glades, lush water meadows and all the other scenes so dear to the heart of the romantic painter, always bathed in sunlight. But Mr. Fingal was, withal, a realist and each painting was meticulously copied from postcards from his vast collection, depicting his currently favoured countryside. Sometimes it might be a desert oasis, but most often it was the English Lake District for green was his favourite colour. These postcards were blown up into canvases of about eighteen inches in length. There was another recurring feature in the Chief Engineer's pictures; figures, always female, never clothed and with poses brushed in with a competence that clearly showed Mr. Fingal's encyclopaedic knowledge of his subject, down to the last seductive curl of pubic hair. He would have doubtless preferred to copy these from life, but he had to content himself with pin ups from the glossy magazines that were in plentiful, although carefully hoarded, supply on board. One further indication of his preferences was that his women were not traditional classic maidens disporting themselves with the innocence of Eve; they were thoroughly modern females, who had discarded every item, even the briefest of seductive nylon underwear before being captured by Mr. Fingal's brush. His detail was, as always, perfect, for not only had he a very logical mind but also as keen an interest in its most intimate coverings as he had in the female form itself, so artfully disposed piles of lingerie were ever present.

These pictures were produced at a rate of one or two per voyage, and as he rarely took any off the ship his cabin was always cluttered with the results of his hobby. He was the living embodiment of the gentleman with etchings. He actually did invite women to come to his cabin to see them, and with a success rate that was the envy of everyone on board. However the paintings were not the only reason; his long years of practice on passenger liners had given him a very sure way with women, and as he only chose the more mature ones he never risked the ridiculous rebuffs of a middle aged man chasing girls young enough to be his daughters.

Another of his interests was race going; he liked the crowds and the atmosphere almost more than the racing itself, for as a punter he was not an unqualified success. It was not that he squandered his money but that the form he preferred to study was female, not equine. However racegoers always remember their wins, never their losses, so Mr. Fingal's tales of the turf, like his passenger liner reminiscences, were full of names dropped and inside knowledge verging on the omniscient. As with his tales of the Homerian and the Olympian there was more than just a grain of truth in some of them. Take for example his visit to the Trots at Melbourne, with his admission that although he studied the flat he knew nothing of trotting; "Gor, I didn't even know enough to tell them from cart horses." was the opening of this oft repeated story. On the Saturday afternoon in question he was among the holiday crowds at the track, wearing his best panama suit, binoculars over one shoulder and an attractive woman leaning against the other. Idly they scanned the list of runners, and there it was, Fingal's Queen in the three thirty. "I must have been the only one daft enough to back such a no hoper, but back her I did - one pound to win." and that is exactly what she did, at the unheard of odds of 610 to 1!

Any description of the Chief Engineer must inevitably centre on his off duty activities rather than his job, for although he was in overall charge of the engines and machinery his staff rarely saw him below. He was the only engineer on board whose boiler suits remained crisply white from the beginning of the trip to its end. Those worn by his subordinates may have started out white but despite incessant dhobying they finished up a muddy grey colour pied with the deeper blotches of oil stains. As with everything else he did this pose was carefully studied. Unless there was an absolute need for his presence he took pains never to be seen 'on the plates'[1], preferring to exercise control through conferences held in the office which adjoined his cabin. However should the occasion so demand he could prove himself a capable enough engineer, but even this had to be a carefully staged performance.

Typical of this was the time the windlass broke down. The ship had left her berth before the tide was high enough to lock out, and as the dock was otherwise empty the anchor was dropped on the bottom at short stay. When the lock master hoisted the signal to proceed the anchor windlass was found to be jammed and refused to lift so much as a single link of chain. The ship had been built before bridge telephones were fitted on tramp ships so this minor mishap gave rise to a confused shouting match between the Captain on the bridge wing and the Chief Mate on the fo'c'sle. Through a megaphone the Captain bellowed his instructions to disconnect the gypsy[2], free run the windlass and connect up again. The Mate could barely make this out above the hubbub on the fo'c'sle head, but when he did he irately clapped his hands to his mouth and yelled back that he had already done that. This exchange took some few minutes by which time the Lock Master and the Pilot were having their own private shouting match to add to the din.

The next instruction from the now heated Captain was to call the Fiver, the junior fifth engineer who kept no watches but was responsible for all the deck machinery. The thoroughly exasperated Mate took some time to take this in, having had to come half way down the fore deck to get within hearing range at all. This was because the shouting matches from bridge to foc's'le and from Pilot to Lock Master had now been augmented by a cacophony of interrogative toots and escaping steam from the tug secured to the bow with full pressure on her boilers but nowhere to go. When eventually the message was received and understood the Mate pointed expressively to the boiler-suited Fiver, who had been summoned at the first sign of trouble and was even now setting his tool box down on the fo'c'sle steampipe casing. Thoroughly roused and totally unable to stand idly by the Captain turned to the Junior Apprentice who was acting as bridge messenger. "Get the Chief".

Mr. Fingal duly appeared, immaculate in his white boiler suit, and typically went straight to the fo'c'sle without proceeding to the bridge for instructions. It was, as it happened, a perfectly simple fault. The windlass was a large, comparatively uncomplicated piece of machinery, but in being elderly, needing a tap here and there with a Monday hammer[3] rather than engineering skill. This would have been well

1. 'on the plates' - *Description given to the gratings which form the engine room floor and walkways*
2. Gypsy - *Cog on the anchor windlass central shaft to take the links of the anchor cable (chain)*
3. Monday Hammer - *Engineer's club hammer used for rough work, of any size larger than a carpenter's hammer*

within the competence of the Fiver, but as befitted his status, the younger man stood back, passing the tools to his chief so that the latter could deliver the single 'coup de grace' that immediately restarted the windlass. Only then, retaining his air of studied deliberation, did the Chief climb to the bridge, his boiler suit still gleaming with laundered whiteness. There he remained in a stance of watchful competence, until the ship finally cleared the lock. Then he retired to his cabin to put the delicate finishing brush strokes to the filmy nylon lingerie discarded by the subject of his latest picture, before adding 'Windlass Overhaul' to his growing defect list.

Chapter 19

**Block Collins,
Able Seaman**

Block shook his head in yet another attempt to clear his befuddled brain. He was responding automatically to the orders being shouted on the fo'c'sle, dimly noting the movements of his new shipmates and dumbly following their actions. He always felt this way on sailing day and was resentful of the authority that made him stand up for'ard in the freezing December cold as the greasy wet piles of West Hartlepool's dock slid astern.

'Bastards.' They were the curse of his life. He was as good as the next man. 'Better in fact.' he thought eyeing the well wrapped backside of the Mate, leaning over the bow, directing operations with imperious waves of his gloved hand. 'All right for him, the supercilious bastard, with his gold braid and stewards to suck up to him when he goes below to his cabin.' Although they had never exchanged more than two words Block already hated the Mate. The Bosun was just as bad, still he had better not try anything on with Block, not this trip, nor on any other.

It was always the same. You were supposed to have rights, just like any other man, but somehow on board ship some bastard made them disappear. It was just work, work, bloody hard work. No wonder you let yourself go in port. Some people could get away with it - that sort did for one - Block's eyes again turned venomously towards the Mate's duffel coated back - but when anyone else tried it on Mr. Bloody Mate and his friends would be the first to drop you in it. Like that snide little twit of a Third Mate a few trips back, blowing his whistle and expecting grown men to come running to the bridge with a 'Yes Sir. No Sir. Three fucking bags full, Sir.' He'd shown that snivelling little git right enough - and the only bloody thanks he got was a logging, a DR[1], and since then all the stinking lousy Pool[2] could do was to give him

1. DR - *Declined Reference entry in Discharge Book*
2. Pool - *The Shipping Federation, which kept a pool of seamen from which ships drew their crews*

pier head jumps[1] on bloody stinking heaps of rusting iron like this.

Morosely Block shambled off the fo'c'sle to sit in surly silence in a corner of the mess room, nursing a hangover and a mug of tea, stewed tea! He'd probably have to fix that little sod of a Peggy[2] before long too. Thus he sat, talking to no one, waiting for his call as First Wheel[3] on the eight to twelve.

The rest of the crowd had sailed from West Hartlepool long enough to be aware of Block's reputation as a real hard case and they knew better than to break into his glowering silence, especially when he had a hangover. Later it would be possible to talk to him, but even then you had to be pretty careful, Block was a big man with a large chip on his shoulder and an ungovernably short fused temper.

The Captain knew of his reputation, as did the Mate; Block's Discharge Book would have spoken for him even had there been no warning from the Shipping Master; "He's an ugly customer, that one, but what can you expect sailing so close to Christmas?" It was a familiar tale; tramp ship life offered a man little inducement at the best of times, and compared with Christmas ashore, none whatsoever. So a crew had to be scraped together from wherever they could be found. As it was a short trip perhaps they might get away with it without too much trouble, but it was a big 'perhaps' as Block's was not the only Discharge Book with more than its fair share of DR entries.

The outward trip was fairly uneventful, although there was some minor trouble with the Bosun. Block continued his surly grumbling whenever he had to work on deck in his regular daytime watches, and predictably enough grumbling even harder if he was not on deck working overtime in his watch below. It was annoying to say the least and went a fair way towards undermining the Bosun's authority, but not far enough to merit a logging from the Captain. There was also the Deck Boy. Block was always yelling "Where's that Bloody Peggy?" if morning coffee was not ready the instant the Bosun called 'Smokoe' and after being threatened with one thumping the Deck Boy went in mortal fear of producing yet another pot of stewed tea for the afternoon break. There had been similar brushes with most of the crowd, but as yet no violence. The presence of such a bully made the closed life of the fo'c'sle uncomfortable, but in the short term not too unbearable to the ship at large. As it was confined to the sailors alone it was, by common consent, a case of letting sleeping dogs lie. Block stood his watch, albeit with little enthusiasm. The Bosun did not feel inclined at this stage to complain to the Mate and thus reveal his own seeming inadequacy; the Deck Boy was too scared to say a word; the Mate felt that to keep a watching brief was the easiest option; and the Captain knowing that there was nothing specific on which he could take action was content not to be drawn in at all at this stage.

This was a situation Block knew only too well. From as far back as he could remember he had been bigger than his fellows, but always the things he had sought

1. Pier head jump - *A casual appointment of a crew member from the dockside just prior to sailing*
2. Peggy - *The most junior seaman, rated Deck Boy, used as the sailor's mess attendant*
3. First Wheel - *First two hours of the watch on the wheel, then one hour as standby, the last hour as look out*

had been kept moving just beyond his reach. School had been a boring waste of time; the official perks went to others with such regularity that it was only by using what was, even then, his considerable strength that he had managed to keep his life from becoming totally void, and its outside world at bay. So it had been throughout his adult life. But there are two sides to every question; whereas to school and workmates alike Block was a sullen bully, to himself he was a normal sort of chap who had just never been given a fair break, whilst everyone else had things handed to them on a plate. He had to fight for everything he ever had, and to fight again to prevent it from then being taken away from him again. What was more, he would continue to fight any and everybody who got in his way. Perhaps this might not be the easiest or the most intelligent way to tackle the world at large, but his present way of life was the only one Block Collins knew.

He drifted in and out of seagoing and its incidents in just the same way he had drifted in and out of every situation he had encountered since childhood. When the going got rough he exploded into a rage, lashed out at everything in his path, suffered the inevitable consequences and finally emerged with an even deeper sense of glowering resentment. Now in his forties, though having a countenance much older, he was a man with no future, almost no friends; to be treated carefully when sober and avoided like the plague when drinking.

On this trip real trouble did not occur until Lagos. By this time the crew were all heartily sick of Block, so whilst they sat around the tables drinking together he stood alone at the bar downing pint after pint in morose silence. It must have been after his fifth or sixth that in straightening up his elbow cleared the counter, glasses and bottles tinkling around his feet. Dumbly he stood and stared at the beer stains spreading over his jeans. "What's the matter, Block, can't you hold it?" piped the Deck Boy, sufficiently emboldened by his two half pints to attempt to pay off old scores. The figure at the bar turned, beer dripping down his legs, his face diffusing with fury, and took a first lurching step towards the suddenly sobered Peggy. "Stow it Block, we all know you're a hard case. So'm I, but just leave the kid alone." He turned to this new threat. That bloody Bosun again! Hard case? That was just one crack too many. He'd met this kind before. "Hard case! Hard case? I'll show you what we do to hard cases where I come from." he bellowed in fury, and seizing the first object to hand he advanced menacingly towards the Bosun.

The bar was suddenly enveloped in a deathly hush, broken only by the smashing of glass as Block struck the bottle he held against the back of a chair. Waving its jagged neck in front of him he moved unsteadily towards the Bosun. For seconds everyone froze, then pandemonium broke out. The press in front of Block parted as if by magic and all he could see was empty space. He turned drunkenly to re-align on his target, but he turned too fast, finishing up sprawled over the nearest table. Neither the Bosun nor the barman were strangers to this type of brawl and both took immediate advantage of this turn of events. The Bosun calmly picked up a half empty pint pot and slugged the prostrate form with enough force to put Block out cold for some hours, the barman meanwhile babbled shrill cries for help down the telephone.

It was all over as suddenly as it had begun, The police arrived and with a familiarity borne of long practice, closed the bar, ordered the crew back to the ship and finally without any pretence of ceremony or care threw the unconscious Block into the back of their jeep. The subsequent formalities were rather more protracted, but their legal platitudes were totally wasted on Block, for he could remember little or nothing of what had happened. Furthermore he was still too hungover to feel anything but resentment at being picked on yet again, this time by his own shipmates. So with his own smouldering sense of injustice intact Block was left behind in a West African gaol. It would be another six months before he again became a problem for the unlucky Captain who would be obliged to take him home as a DBS[1].

---

1. DBS - *Distressed British Seaman; a UK seafarer who missed his ship due to sickness or jail was, by law, forced upon the master of the next UK registered ship homeward bound through the port*

Chapter 20

**Alan Brown,
Second Engineer**

Everyone knew that the Second was mad. Not insane mad, but just an irrepressible character who would never conform. Around him life rarely had any dull moments.

During his apprenticeship at a Wallsend shipyard he was always the central figure in any horseplay, the rougher the better. He was the one who played the time honoured stunt of 'welding the chamber pot' which tended to replace the ancient custom of 'topping out' new building. But being Alan, the traditional masthead was not for him; he showed his originality by affixing it to the deck under the Captain's chair in the saloon. It was he also who rode a ramshackle motor bike around the yard with no brakes and a sublime disregard for road safety. It was typical of Alan that he never had an accident; others yes, but Alan Brown, never. Nor was he ever picked up by the police although his road tax was always months out of date.

As a sea-going Engineer he did not change. He was physically big, and so could manhandle tools and machine parts with a gay abandon that would have cost others skinned knuckles at the very least, possibly even mangled limbs. For all that, he was an engineer to the tips of his blunt, oil smeared fingers; perhaps not overstrong on theory, but supremely confident of his ability to coerce engines into working co-operation with the aid of a Monday hammer and a cold chisel. He progressed rapidly from Fifth to Third Engineer, but then he met his first setback. Further promotion meant sitting for a ticket. He balked at this fence time and time again, almost regressing from being the youngest, keenest Third in the company to being an 'also ran', but he was saved in the nick of time by the oldest trick in the book, an ambitious woman.

Joanne's family had been at sea for generations, and she had been educated at the Royal Merchant Navy School at Winnersh in Berkshire - her father lost at sea in the war had qualified her for a place. She knew what she wanted - Alan, but not as a run of the mill Third Engineer. She made Alan's choice abundantly clear; Joanne and a Second's ticket or else. So he went back again to college. It was a hard grind, his thick Geordie accent was as unwieldy with engineering theory as his hands were articulate with hammer and chisel. It took three attempts, three months at college, interspersed each time with the three months sea-time imposed after each failure, but in the end he made it. His wedding photographs showed him standing in an unaccustomed uniform with three brand new gold stripes, with a grin at once both smug and self conscious, beside his diminutive bride. That however was the last they saw of each other for some time. His next homecoming was to a wife with a six month old daughter.

Neither promotion nor family ties sobered him in any way. He was still the life and soul of every shipboard party, especially if beer was involved, and it was the Second Engineer who was the moving spirit behind any social innovation in the closed life of the ship. Water skiing was one of his ideas. The ship was at anchor off Rangitoto Island during one of New Zealand's perennial dock strikes and off duty time lay heavily on everyone's hands. So Alan decided to use the one motor lifeboat to enliven proceedings. At first the old man was sceptical, but he could see the sense of getting the boat into the water, and eventually agreed. The first problem was to get her launched; the boat and the davits were so caked up with paint, rust and disuse that it took the combined efforts of the Second and the Carpenter even to swing her over the side. Then she took all of three days to take up enough to be baled dry, for which task the Second borrowed the two Apprentices, much to their disgust. Once the boat was dry the sport should have proceeded, but no, the immersion in salt water on top of its previous rusting rendered the engine as cold as yesterday's news. However Alan was now in his element and over the side he went with hammer, chisel and monkey wrench. He had the engine sparking and spluttering before lunch, but unfortunately his affinity was for machinery, not woodwork, so proceedings were held up yet again. This time it took two days for Chippy to repair the planking holed by the Second's less than delicate attention to the cylinder head. The skis produced by the carpenter were adequate if somewhat clumsy. The shoes created by the Bosun were less expert, being merely spliced loops of inch and a half sisal, but the Second was confident that they would serve. They did, only too well, shrinking rapidly on their first contact with the water to hold Alan's ankles in a vice-like grip quite unlike the quick release shoes fitted to proper water skis.

This might have mattered little but for one thing which everyone had overlooked; Merchant navy lifeboats are designed for range and endurance, not speed. They can provide only about half that needed to get ski-borne, no more. The result was the never to be forgotten spectacle of the Second being towed around the harbour, half submerged, his ankles firmly imprisoned in the rope loops, his position clearly marked by the wash from his upturned skis. That was the end of that particular sport on board. Fortunately the cost was no more than a pair of rope chafed ankles; its real value was that it had provided the crew with a welcome break from the tedium over two whole weekends marooned at anchor in an outer roadstead.

Alan's escapades were all centred around machinery and his uncanny knack of being able to abuse it and come away unscathed. Some were concerned with off duty activities, but many were strictly practical. For example, when there was a foul hawse and the windlass jammed solid it was the Second who went over the bow in a bosun's chair with sledge and blow torch to break and free the cable. This task he performed in record time whilst swinging to and fro on the end of a line in pouring rain. This would have been noteworthy in itself, but the chain had not been properly secured on the fo'c'sle head, so when the end was finally freed some dozen links weighing nearly a hundredweight apiece came crashing down on the swinging figure below. It was typical that whereas anyone else would have been killed, the chain whistled past Alan, wrenching the sledge hammer out of his hands but leaving him completely without a scratch.

However such jobs were not generally the lot of the Second Engineer. He was the senior watchkeeper and as such was also responsible for the general maintenance of the engine room. In port steam for the deck machinery was maintained on one boiler, so fire in the other two could be drawn. This released most of the firemen from watch-keeping and they were employed by the Second on preventive maintenance and minor running repairs, but there were occasionally other jobs. One of the most popular of these was painting, as it was so completely different from all the other engine room tasks. An almost holiday atmosphere prevailed, the firemen laughing and talking with over loud self conscious voices. The paint brushes they wielded were as unfamilar to them as the unstable scaffolding from which they worked. Certainly their efforts were not as professional as the deck crowd, often as much paint was splattered on the gratings below as was brushed on the bulkheads themselves. The finished result was always replete with runs and holidays, but as they would be covered by a fresh film of soot and coal dust within days it did not matter. Anyway, the object of the exercise was not to beautify the engine room but to keep corrosion at bay for another few months.

It was Alan's job to plan all this, and to order up the stores necessary to carry it out. His store room had to be replenished whenever the ship reached a home port, where the Second had to account for all the stores expended, and to re-order them. A Defects List was formally required from the Chief Engineer, but the hard work of compiling it was done by the Second Engineer. It kept him busy all his off watch hours for weeks before the end of each voyage. This was the one time that Alan, normally very outward, going became rather harassed and morose. Paper work had never been his strong point and the parsimonious economy enforced by the owners was alien to his bluff open handed nature. By the time the battle with his Stores and Defects Lists was complete the Second was more than ready for his all too brief leave. The regulations allowed him an annual leave of fourteen days plus an extra day for every Sunday at sea, but this was always providing that the ship was in port long enough, and that he could be spared from the vital tasks that had to be performed during her stay.

It was this that finally terminated Alan's sea career. It was not the Company's policy to provide relieving crews so that their sea-going officers might have the full benefit of their time in home ports. This meant that both the Chief and the Second needed to be on board for the first two or three days in port and for the same time prior to sailing. The rest of the time they could split, one on leave, the other standing by the ship; that is except for one day in the middle when both had to be on board for a handover. As the ship was rarely in the UK for more than three weeks at a time Alan would be lucky to get a week at home more than once in any one year. With a growing family he felt that he should play a more important part in his home than that of an infrequent visitor, and so despite the attractions of a relatively carefree life at sea he finally came ashore for good.

Chapter 21

**Bill Andrews,
AB**

In any city there are thousands upon thousands of insignificant people who quite easily disappear in a crowd. In the countryside it is less easy for a villager to submerge. A smaller, more closely knit community ensures that each individual is assigned a real personality, however colourless. At sea with the even tighter bonds of ship board inter-dependence it is impossible for anyone to disappear in a crew of less than fifty souls. Yet Bill Andrews did just this! Ashore you would only realise he was with the crew when you counted heads to order a round. At sea you only became aware of him when everyone had been given a paint pot and brush, but there was still a spare unissued set and one man waiting to be issued, Bill Andrews.

Bill had made AB only because he had held an EDH ticket for four years. He would never make Bosun. How he had ever got his ticket in the first place was somewhat questionable, for although he had just enough competence to avoid being a poor seaman, he could certainly never have passed any examination in the normal course of events. Maybe the Gods were kind on the day when Bill sat, maybe when the examiner counted up his passes and failures there was one man he simply could not remember having seen at all, maybe there had been no crashing failures that day. So maybe by giving the extra man the benefit of the doubt, Bill was included in the passes. Be that as it may he became an EDH and as he never seemed to do anything good or bad he made AB in the fullness of time, a rate he seemed likely to hold with the standard 'VG'[1] discharge for both conduct and ability until the day he died.

On board Bill was always the odd man out; in a three man watch the other two automatically paired off as companions for the voyage. He was not so much solitary, it was just that he did not seem to be there at all. Rarely did he join in mess room conversation, nor did he go ashore unless it was one of those runs that involved the whole crowd. The only occasion he came alive was when the talk

1. VG - *Discharge Books gave a seaman two references at the end of a trip, one for conduct, one for ability. These references were limited to two options - VG (Very Good) or DR (Declined Reference)*

came around to wives and families. Then he would become quite animated though a trifle repetitious.

Given any opportunity he would snatch a battered wallet from the back pocket of his dungarees and slap it down on the table, its collection of dog-eared snapshots overflowing. In all of these Mrs. Bill Andrews was the central figure, for they had no children. Perhaps this was to be expected for she was of the same nature as her husband. No matter how many times you saw these, afterwards you could remember only their backgrounds; the house, New Brighton Beach, Blackpool Tower; but of Mrs. Andrews you would have only a very hazy recollection, or more likely none at all. I have even been forced to refer to the lady as Mrs. Bill Andrews; she did have a christian name to which Bill constantly referred, but it was just another of those things about Bill that could not be recalled after an interval of a very few moments. So as I said before, Bill's conversation was animated, but not inspired. A fair sample would go: "Yes, I'm married." "Last leave we had a smashing time at Blackpool." "That's her in this picture." "I can't think what on earth she sees in a chap like me." We could all agree with Bill's last statement, but only up to a point; it was equally hard to imagine what he saw in her. On balance they must have been a particularly well suited couple.

At sea Bill's only relaxation appeared to be filling sheet after sheet of cheap notepaper with his laborious handwriting. His only pleasure was to receive equally long replies in Mrs. Andrew's neat, featureless script. When he opened his mail he would sit alone in the corner of the mess room, a smile on his face, his lips slowly forming each word as he savoured by proxy his domestic bliss.

However on this one trip all was not well. Although the letters still came the smile was missing from his face as his lips slowly traced each written word. As port succeeded port Bill became more and more anxious to get his mail, and, if that was possible, became more quiet than before. After steaming back and forth across the oceans for seven months Bill was really at a low ebb. He seldom had had much to say, now he never spoke at all. His face for once began to take on some character, but this was not a good sign. Whereas previously he had passed unnoticed, now his deep ringed eyes with their haunted look betrayed a man stretched almost beyond his limits. Still Singapore was our next port and after that only the bunkering stops at Colombo, Aden and Port Said separated us from home.

For once in his life Bill Andrews took an interest in the day's run, but it was a feverish one, not the normal healthy forerunner of the Channels[1], for we were still over a month from home. Nevertheless Bill began buttonholing the Third Mate after dinner to find out just how many more days before we reached the UK, and in the mess he began to talk again, discussing worriedly exactly what sort of delays we might encounter.

1. Channels - *The restlessness that grips the whole crew when entering the English Channel homeward bound*

It was after leaving Singapore that his tortured mind reached its point of no return. His mail had been even lighter than usual, but it took him longer to digest it, his emotional load having slowed his speed of reading to near zero. He was quite normal until we sailed but then a buzz started; we were not homeward bound after all, but bound for Australia to load grain. In his troubled imaginings Bill was slowly being driven frantic as each beat of the screw took him remorselessly further away from England. He sat slumped in the corner of the mess, whey faced and muttering, for at least two long hours. Then suddenly he sprang up with an agonised cry, and dashed out on deck weaving his way amidships like a madman.

The two off watch sailors, for once becoming aware of his presence, rushed out after him. Bill's screamed "I must go home" warned them that he intended to do something drastic. Normally he would have been easily outdistanced, but with a frenetic burst of speed he stayed a good ten feet ahead of them and taking the bridge steps three at a time, was inside before they could so much as shout a warning. The steady throb of the engines ceased abruptly as the bells clanged 'Stop' and Bill was revealed hanging with all his might to the brass handles of the engine room telegraph.

"Turn her round. Turn her round." was all he could yell as both the Mate and the Captain attempted to pull him away, but such was his maniacal strength that their combined efforts could not even budge him.

All this took only seconds. The helmsman just looked on dumbfounded, absently twirling the spokes of the unresponsive wheel as the ship rapidly lost steerage way and veered dangerously toward the edge of the narrow fairway. The two sailors had by now reached the bridge but were incapable of anything beyond gaping wide eyed at this unprecedented scene. Clearly something had to be done before the ship grounded, but everyone seemed frozen to the spot except for the three figures wrestling about the telegraph. "Turn her round. Turn her round" screamed the tormented AB. "Turn her round. Turn her round." He thrashed about, arms and legs striking out wildly at the two officers, when suddenly the Mate, with blood streaming from a cut lip was flung bodily against the starboard bulkhead. The resounding crash as he hit the panelling seemed to break the spell. Bill Andrews abruptly let go of the telegraph and collapsed whimpering into the corner, the Captain swung the telegraph back to 'Full ahead' and the bells clanged forth as the ship once again began to gather way. For the next few minutes everyone was far too busy to spare a glance for the pathetic figure crouched behind them, crying pitifully and muttering between sobs "I must go home, she needs me, she needs me."

There was little anyone could do. Clearly Bill, pushed beyond his modest limits had cracked and broken. He did however get home, but under medical supervision and only after spending many more months in a Singapore mental hospital. Afterwards he was totally unfit for any further seagoing; indeed it is doubtful whether he ever again really recognised his wife, or their son, born without the support he had thought she needed so desperately.

We did in fact have to 'turn her round' to off load him on to the port health ambulance launch. And Australia for grain? That was just a buzz, we continued homeward bound direct to Liverpool, Bill's native port.

Chapter 22

Jacob Hamilton,
Stowaway

"You realise that you have committed a serious crime, and that I must sentence you to thirty days in gaol."

This statement made about as much sense as a lecture on the evils of gambling to a lottery winner. Jacob had made it, as the ear splitting grin on his homely black face showed. As he had papers proving him to be a citizen of the British Commonwealth, both he and the judge knew that on his release he would be able to stay in a Britain flowing with milk and honey, where there were both jobs for those who wished to work and financial assistance for the unemployed. Not that Jacob had any intention of joining the ranks of the latter; he was young, fit and heartily sick of the occasional casual labour that kept him below the poverty line in his own homeland. My last sight of Jacob was as he disappeared below the dock with his gaoler, leaving me behind in the dusty court room; but like the Cheshire Cat, his grin seemed to remain.

In the few weeks Jacob had been on board he had won grudging approval from everyone, he was patently more than willing to work his passage, and never lost his widespread grin, not even when the Captain raged at him on their first meeting two days out at sea. For Jacob was a stowaway, secreted on board despite the most careful twenty-four hour gangway watch in port and a thorough search before sailing. Quite understandably the Captain was furious, but to Jacob it was the first victory in a long, very carefully planned campaign.

There were always plenty of attempts to stow away, but most were unsuccessful. Coming aboard with the last of the cargo it was nigh on impossible to hide carefully enough to avoid discovery. Jacob knew this, he had tried twice before. Once he got put ashore whilst the ship was still alongside; the second time he was returned on the pilot boat and arrested as soon as he touched his home soil again, after less than a one hour round voyage. This nearly put paid to his ambitions as it identified him to the Harbour Police as a persona non grata on the docks, but Jacob was a very determined young man. His third attempt was much better planned. He decided that a last minute dash on board and a quick scrabble underneath the top layer of sacks was doomed to failure. In order to remain undetected a more carefully chosen hiding place was required. This would take time, and could not easily be done without attracting too much attention. So Jacob scraped together his pitifully limited supply of cash and entrusted it to one of his many cousins who just happened to know the girlfriend of the brother of the wharf foreman. This judicious placement of his capital gave Jacob the opportunity to construct a hide that would remain undetected, not leave him crushed under too many tiers of sacks, until the voyage was at least forty eight hours old, by which time no captain would not consider turning back to put him ashore.

In the graveyard watch of the third day, but quite unconscious of any symbolism, a ghostly apparition clad in a long, once white robe, arose from the starboard ventilator trunking of number two hold. But for once the wire grills were securely in place thus barring the emergent figure from access to the deck. His shouts first reached the fo'c'sle for the wind was from aft and the ventilator cowls were trimmed forward. They made the lookout's heart skip a beat, for Jacob, despite his size, had a very high pitched voice, and when raised to a shout it became a very animal-like scream.

Jacob had no clothes but the cotton robe he wore, no possessions and judging by the way he ravenously wolfed down a hunk of bread, no food. It appeared when the Captain interrogated him that he had no papers either, so the Official Log entry recorded the time of discovery and the terse comment; 'Name stated to be Jacob Hamilton.' A bed was found for him in the empty cabin designated as the Ship's Hospital, and at nine o'clock next day he was turned over to the Bosun. All hands were used to stowaways, they lived and ate separately from the crew, and almost never had adequate clothing. It was a legal requirement that they must be fed and housed at the ship's expense, hence the Captain's anger, but whether they fed as well as the rest of the crew and whether any odd items of surplus clothing supplemented their meagre stores before the cold weather of the Bay, was dependent on their willingness to work. It was rough justice, but a lazy stowaway would be a very cold and very hungry stowaway when handed over to the UK authorities. Jacob had a fat well fed sheen and an adequate, if rather variegated wardrobe by the time the ship docked in Hull. By then he had consumed prodigious quantities of food, for never in all his life could he remember such plenty; second helpings at all meals with as much bread as he could cram in, seemed to Jacob like Christmas every day of the week. He was now utterly convinced that the stories of high life and fantastic wealth that had lured him towards the Mother Country must be true.

He was not even dispirited when the Captain, who by now felt some sympathy towards his unwanted guest, warned him that without papers he would be unable to enter Britain, and would be 'repatriated forthwith'. Jacob was not altogether sure that he understood these two long words, for English was not his mother tongue, but his grin was unaltered. He knew that he had not come so far only to be disappointed on the final threshold. Locking Jacob into the hospital cabin to prevent him making a run for it as soon as the ship docked was a completely unnecessary precaution. The moment a uniformed and obviously British policeman entered the cabin, Jacob in his ragged best, with his woolly hair smartly combed, drew himself up to his full height, and said "Jacob Hamilton, Sir. I am a British subject; here are my papers." This was Jacob's trump card. Undisclosed for weeks despite the captain's anger and the crew's friendship, this tattered scrap of paper must have remained intimately concealed about his person, its very existence never even suspected. It would now ensure his permanent entry into his personal Promised Land and what was the standard thirty day prison sentence compared to that? Impossibly his grin spread even wider, taking in ears, eyes and every other inch of skin on his ecstatic black face as he marched triumphantly ashore into the waiting squad car.

Chapter 23

Warren Fitzroy, Bosun

The Bosun was a huge man, well over six feet tall, yet he gave the impression of being even larger still. He hailed from the Bahamas and, like many other of his countrymen, gloried in a name flamboyant to my English middle class ears. He was Warren Emerson Fitzroy. There was little employment on his home island, so from the age of sixteen he had been at sea, sailing under many different flags but, since becoming a Bosun some years earlier, he had shipped exclusively out of Cardiff on British tramp ships, become a member of the Pool and between voyages lived with his mistress of the moment in Tiger Bay.

The Mate was responsible for the maintenance of the ship, the Bosun was his foreman. Warren controlled the sailors with humour, his surprisingly high pitched voice continually bubbling into laughter; but he combined this with force of personality - It was always quite clear that he intended his orders to be carried out. He was also thoroughly competent at his job and when the work demanded it he was the first to muck in; on many an occasion his strength had been the saving factor in tricky situations.

This physical strength also had domestic advantages, especially after rowdy nights ashore when the returning crew were not always on their best behaviour. There was one Ordinary Seaman, Joseph, a coffee skinned Seychelloise who, when drunk, inevitably decided on purely racial grounds that he belonged amidships, not aft. The result was that as regular as clockwork he finished up outside the Mate's cabin singing the Pater Noster in a French patois, following the performance with maudlin demands to be allowed to share the cabin rather than live with 'those black bastards' down aft. The solution was standard - "Send for the Bosun." On arrival Warren used to pick up the protesting seaman, tucking him effortlessly under one arm like a small child, and walk off aft without pause, despite Joseph clinging with all his might to every stanchion and door jamb they passed. This was no mean feat, for Joseph himself was a hefty, near six footer.

The Bosun was the wealthiest man aft. This was not due entirely to his higher wages but to his skill at cards. Whenever subs were issued in a foreign port he drew only a modest sum, but within a very short space of time he relieved the poker school of enough of its cash to finance his own runs ashore. His skill was legendary, but his consistent run of luck verged on the miraculous; he had never been known to lose. It was half suspected that he played with marked cards; indeed several people had suggested it to his face, but he was far too canny to be called out on that one. He would laugh, crinkle his features into a huge grin and look just too transparently honest. Anyway he was far too big for anyone to contemplate further action. The only recourse was not to play poker with Warren Fitzroy, which did not offend him in the slightest for there were always plenty of others willing. He was once asked by a non-playing friend how it was done and half seriously he made the offer, "Well Third, you give me all you earn for three years, and I'll teach you all I know." Warren, I quite often wish I had taken you up.

These poker games allowed the Bosun to really indulge himself ashore. You could usually find him in the better hotels or nightclubs, elegantly suited, always with a girl on his arm, often with one on each. Some men have charm and a little spare money, a few lucky ones are irresistible to women and have cash aplenty, Warren Fitzroy was one of these latter and he exploited it to the full. Nor was he reticent about it, and it provided many another excuse for his infectious laughter; but sometimes his puckish humour rebounded.

A classic case of this occurred in Sydney, in the days when the White Australia policy was not quite dead and non-white British seamen were not always fully welcomed. The ship was lying out in stream and the crew were being ferried ashore in the same launch as the Customs Officers who had cleared her inwards. There was the usual cheerful banter concerning past exploits in King's Cross and expectations for the coming evening. Warren was leading this exchange, his ebullient manner drawing attention to himself, and inevitably to the somewhat bulky package he was carrying under his arm. "What have you got there?" "Oh, nothing man, that's just French letters, man; I've got a heavy date tonight." he chuckled. "Open it." in that aggressive twang that only Australian Customs Officers can manage when they think they are being set up. As before stated the Bosun was nothing if not honest. Everyone except the discountenanced official dissolved into fits of laughter when the unwrapped package revealed itself to be as Warren stated, a large cache of condoms. Unfortunately Warren, in his moment of triumph, uncharacteristically over played his hand, "I'm just fucking mad, man." he chuckled rolling his eyes with feigned innocence. That really fixed the Bosun. It took the Customs Officers two hours to go through every item Warren had about him, then he was sent back to the ship and the same scrutiny accorded to his cabin. Although they found nothing, the search was capped by the Bosun's official restriction to the ship for the whole time she remained in an Australian port.

However that was only one occasion. Most of the time Warren led a charmed existence. With his deep musical chuckle he use to say "Man I intend to die of old age; I'll just be shot by a jealous husband when I'm too fat and old to dive out the window before he takes good aim." I think he might just be right too.

Chapter 24

**Old Jan,
AB**

Jan, or rather Old Jan as he was now universally known, was inappropriately named for he hailed from the Western Isles, not the West Country. Yet he had been Jan for almost as long as he could remember, in fact ever since he first left the inshore fishing boats of his native Stornoway for the deep sea fisheries of the Humber. There his quiet, slow, highland rendering of his given name, John, had instantly and unquestioningly been accepted as Jan by ears more attuned to rougher North Country accents - Jan he had been ever since. At first he had vaguely resented it, for he was proud of his homeland and his ancestry of countless crofting generations, then he came to regard it with an amused tolerance, now he answered to no other name.

It had been a hard life crofting and fishing, there were few spare pence when Jan went to school. One of his earliest memories was sliding down slopes on the seat of his pants in a desperate effort to wear out a set of an older brother's hand me downs. The frustration of thus trying to ruin real hand woven Harris tweed, and the near impossibility of convincing his mother that the result was fair wear and tear, were still remembered, as was the feel of the hand of his disbelieving parent on his backside. Although he had worked about the croft almost from the time he could walk Jan was not allowed to go on fishing trips until he was twelve. An unnecessary delay Jan thought, for he had been convinced of his ability to pull and haul with the menfolk since his ninth birthday.

It was a hard school. Seamanship of the first order was demanded, although but poorly rewarded. With several other siblings and only the one small croft to support them all it was almost a foregone conclusion that Jan could not stay at home and hope to wrest a living from his beloved island. Sentimentalists may bemoan the depopulation of the Islands, but for Jan and many others of his generation it was not the lure of easy money in the big cities, it was sheer necessity that forced them out, not greed that egged them on. So Jan left to take up the only trade he knew, fishing. For years he sailed on drifters and deep sea trawlers, even during the war his Royal

Navy service had been spent on a coastal minesweeper that was itself a converted trawler. However fishing, even on the most modern freezer trawlers is a younger man's job, and so shortly after his fiftieth birthday Jan forsook the Humber, became Old Jan and signed on deep sea.

On a tramp ship a sailor like Old Jan was something of a rarity. He must have been the only man on board who found the life luxurious. After the conditions on trawlers he found the accommodation spacious, the food excellent, the hours of work ideal and being away from from the continual cold dampness of a fish deck a welcome relief. There was no daywork in the fishing fleet, it was watch on, stop on when hauling. Here on the tramp ship Jan, as the most competent sailor, was the dayworker, the Bosun's right hand man. Never before in all his forty odd years of seafaring had the old fisherman had a nine to five job, with Saturday afternoons off and all day Sunday as well.

Jan was the only dayworker, for the ship could only muster a total of eleven sailors all told, three on each of the three watches, a Deck Boy as the Peggy and Old Jan. The Board of Trade complement was twelve, but on this trip she was not fully manned as she had sailed only days before Christmas when seamen, especially the married ones, would fabricate almost any excuse to avoid signing on. As well as working with the crowd on deck Jan acted as the Bosun's storekeeper. On a larger ship he might even have been dignified with the title of Lamptrimmer. It was he who mixed the paint in its ten gallon drums, stirring the thick porridge like mixture with an old broom handle until its consistency was satisfactorily thinned to his economic highland man's eye, and then carefully ladled into the crew's paint cans with an old corned beef tin. It was also Jan's job to ensure that the brushes the crew returned at five o'clock were first cleaned off in paraffin and then stood in a can of freshwater in order to keep their bristles supple for the next day.

It was Jan who did all the wire splicing too. Officially any of the ABs could have done it, it was part of the syllabus for their EDH tickets. In practice few could, and none so fast and effectively as Jan. This was a direct result of his years fishing, where unless broken gear could be spliced rapidly and efficiently the boat would be out of the fish before the gear could be shot again, or it would part again as soon as any load was placed on it. Not only could he splice wire, he could do it in several different ways as well. For derrick runners he favoured a locking splice, for springs a straight splice with the lay. Rarely with wire rope did Jan use the Royal Navy's chosen method of splicing against the lay. He maintained that this method could cause serious weaknesses. In this he may or may not have been right, but certainly none of Old Jan's splices ever gave the slightest trouble.

As a dayworker he took no regular tricks at the wheel, that was left to the watchkeepers, but entering or leaving port the 'pilot wheel' was always taken by the more experienced ABs in rotation, irrespective of watches. As all hands would be turned out on overtime for entering or leaving harbour, it did not matter if the man at the wheel was not one of the watch on deck. Jan took his place in this rota, and as he was out and away the best helmsman on board he usually had the wheel in all the most difficult harbour approaches. He seemed to have an instinctive way of anticipating the pilot's intentions and of the ship's changing response to the helm at reduced speeds. Jan was also quiet, unhurried and completely unflappable, a very sound combination to have at the wheel in those ports where pilots were apt to have a less than perfect command of the English language, and exhibited a tendency to explode into tirades in a foreign tongue whenever they became excited.

For all his seafaring experience Jan was not widely travelled. Before going deep sea his fishing voyages had begun and ended in home ports with only occasional visits to the Faeroes, Iceland or Norway when stormbound or in need of emergency repairs, never with much chance of shore leave. In the wartime Royal Navy he had been nowhere except up and down the east coast of the British Isles. So although Old Jan had been at sea since before most of the crew were born he had really seen very little of the world. Thus he could still take a simple delight in seeing new countries and places whilst the younger men were already so blasé that they rarely moved out beyond the dockside bars and taverns.

In one other way he stood out from the rest of the crew in his shoregoing. On board he was, like all of them, invariably attired in dungarees and a checked woollen shirt, but unlike them he never wore these clothes ashore. Wet or fine, hot or cold, Jan always wore a navy blue serge suit tightly buttoned across his ample waistline, a tie of his own clan tartan which sartorially screamed at the pale blue stripes of his shirt and the dark navy of his jacket, a cloth cap and highly polished black boots. This made him conspicuous in every port of the world, except perhaps in his native Stornoway where every man of his generation possessed a nearly identical outfit for Sunday best. Not that this mode of dress caused Jan any concern, for as far back as he could remember it had been the correct dress of all the substantial citizens of his home island. Confident in his own upbringing he would continue to wear it, no matter what.

This was typical of Old Jan's whole approach to life. You were taught the right way to do things, you learned the lesson thoroughly and then practiced it without fear or favour. In return, provided you kept to the rules, life treated you fairly as a rule. It was a simple straight forward philosophy, but then Old Jan was a simple straight forward man; contented and at one with his world.

Chapter 25

**Mick Townside,
Third Mate**

The Board of Trade laid down strict regulations about lifeboat rations, and a traditional task for the Third Mate was to ensure that these were complied with, so Mick Townside was making his regular once a voyage check. Up on the boat deck it was hot and very grimy, smoke from the funnel continuously sweeping down on the canvas covers of the lifeboats, making the material harsh enough to scrape the skin off any exposed back. So even in the Mediterranean summer Mick was wearing a thick old khaki shirt as he delved under the wooden strong backs and soot encrusted boat covers.

The check was made homeward bound because there was always the chance that a Board of Trade Inspector would ask the lifeboat gear to be mustered. For the last week or so of the voyage the emergency stores would probably be safe enough from being purloined. The boats water tanks were dry, but that was in order, for despite the legal requirement they were never filled at sea because the water would go stale far to quickly. It would be time enough to fill them a few days before arrival in a home port. The correct number of tins of biscuit were still there for they were particularly unpalatable, you could not even give them away when they became time expired. The milk was a couple of tins short, but that was no more than you would expect on a tramp ship provisioned on a strict 'pound and pint' allowance. The barley sugar was also well down, very likely the result of the check made by the apprentices on leaving the UK six months previously.

It never worried anyone that the lifeboat stores were not fully on top line. In a peacetime emergency you could always store up well before abandoning ship and with modern radio communications you would never be in the boats for more than a few hours. What was probably more important was the lack of some of the other gear.

An inventory of axes, knives and parachute flares was laid down in the Statutory Instruments, but was never complete in the boats except just before the Quadrennial Inspection in dry dock. The combination of economy and inertia common to the storing cycle of a tramp ship ensured they never would be. The most important thing about the check to Mick was that the inventory became thus more readily learned by rote, so that it could be glibly trotted out when he sat for his next Ticket at the end of this trip.

The Third Mate completed his check, re-secured the grimy cover and started on the after starboard boat. The ship had four lifeboats, but this was the only one equipped with engine and radio. Of course the radio was not actually there. It was kept with battery fully charged, in Spark's cabin. The engine had never been known to start without at least a day's work on it by the Fiver. However it was the only boat known to be seaworthy and with falls[1] that could be guaranteed not to be too paint clogged to run freely, because Number Three Boat was put into the water and used fairly frequently. In fact, anytime the ship was anchored off, it was lowered and used for essential journeys between ship and shore to save money, the ship's accounting only allowing enough slack for the Captain to use the more luxurious launch provided by the ship's agent.

By 1500 he had finished the last boat. His deficiency list completed, he went back to his cabin to await the steward with his afternoon cup of tea. It was not the usual de-personalised accommodation provided by the company. Mick had joined the Wolf Cubs at seven and gone through all the various grades right up to Rover Crew, and had latterly become one of the very select few Deep Sea Scouts, as the badge on his wrist band proudly showed. This was reflected in the way that his personal possessions and changes to the company's standard cabin decor had created in miniature the general impression of the den of an adult Boy Scout. Scouting was also where he had acquired his major spare time interest. The 9th (St.Harold's) Plaistow Troop had a long tradition of amateur theatricals and, although no singer, Mick Townside was part of that tradition. As well as being Stage Manager and Handyman he had for many years been 'Spear Carrier in Chief' for their Gilbert and Sullivan seasons. From this had grown a passion for the Savoy operas; he knew almost every one by heart. His collection of books on their every aspect travelled with him around the globe and necessitated his owning three large trunks for his gear when everyone else needed but two. He also nursed a secret ambition to be employed by the D'Oyly Carte Opera Company, no matter how lowly the position. The only time this particular hobby came to the notice of his shipmates was when it entered one of its periodic creative phases. He attempted to write lyrics for comic operettas based on the ship and its crew, matched in artistic quality only by the enthusiasm with which he recited them to anyone who would listen.

1. Falls - *Rope tackles with pully blocks to provide a 'geared' mechanism for lowering the ship's boats*

This was not true of Mick's other sea going hobby. The whole crew was constantly being made aware of it, for somewhere along the line he had acquired a passion for the bagpipes, despite having not a drop of Celtic blood in his veins. He had also acquired a set, which after many years of practice he could very nearly master, and it was not unusual to see his lonely figure silhouetted against the sunset marching back and forth across the fo'c'sle accompanied by the most eldritch sounds conceivable.

These interests would have been unusual in his native South East London, at sea they were almost, if not quite unique. Certainly I have never heard of any other bagpiping cockney Savoyard shipping out as a Third Mate. In a seafaring world, where few had any hobbies at all, this made Mick a character in his own right. It had also been of great service to his career. With his background and education the Merchant Navy could only offer him a start as a laundry boy on a large passenger liner. Not a very auspicious beginning for someone who even then intended to become a Ship's captain some day. By sheer perseverence, helped by his unusual hobby, he had brought himself to the notice of the Bosun and after three trips he re-signed as a Deck Boy and moved to the sailor's mess to avoid being ridiculed out of the even more unusual activity of studying for a Second Mate's Ticket from a glory hole bunk. It took a long time, plus an almost inconceivable degree of dedication, and at least three failed attempts, but at last he achieved his goal. He was perhaps older than most newly promoted Third Mates, but for him the bridge of a tramp ship was a world away from his terraced back street home. Anyway he was not too old. Five, or maybe ten, more years of ceaseless study and he could well be in line for command; that is unless his wildest ambition was realised and he was offered a chance to walk on in a D'Oyly Carte production carrying a spear.

Unfortunately neither avenue opened for him, he slipped and fell down an open hatch in Liverpool, was invalided home in a wheel chair, which for many years since has propelled him down to the Scout Hut from which he started, on every Tuesday and Friday evening; thankful that his third ambition, to be a Scouter, is one not denied to paraplegics. But a wheelchair bound bagpiping Savoyard in a Scout Master's uniform? Knowing Mick's persistence, he may even yet wheel himself on stage in a revival of Pinafore, complete with bagpipes and spear.

Chapter 26

**Reggie Baker,
First Mate**

Some people are destined to be square pegs in round holes and Reggie Baker was definitely one of them. He would have been just as much out of place on a farm or in an office as he was at sea. After a very conventional grammar school education he had left his native Devon to join the Merchant Navy for no very good reason, yet for lack of any other he had stayed on, progressing slowly, very slowly upward. Now, in late middle age he had climbed as far as he would ever go as First Mate on a rather elderly tramp ship.

Each successive crew quickly adopted a nickname for Reggie. 'Eustace' after the Daily Mirror cartoon character was a fair example. A more unusual one was 'Bezel'. The glass on the bridge telegraph had broken and Reggie had dredged up a piece nearly the right size, but had no glass cutter, so in the saloon one day he asked the Chief Steward if he could borrow the rather flashy diamond ring the latter always wore 'in order to cut the bezel to fit the telegraph glass'. Though possibly not so stupid as it might seem, the apprentices who had never heard the word used before could not withhold their laughter and 'Bezel' it was from that day until signing off. Not that these nicknames were ever used to his face, for traditionally he rated the title 'Mr. Mate' from his right hand man the Bosun and 'Sir' from the Apprentices, but to me he will always be affectionately remembered as 'Bezel'.

As Mate Reggie had to programme the deck maintenance so that the Bosun acting as his foreman could set the sailors to work on it. Secretly the Mate would have been far happier working with the crowd rather than organising them, and he had in fact taken upon himself the maintenance of the bridge woodwork. In common with many ships built in the thirties the bridge was open, with a chest high teak screen around it, the box-like wheelhouse on the after end of the bridge was also teak, and the screen was repeated on the Captain's deck below. This expanse of wood was Reggie's pride and joy. He had painstakingly taught generations of apprentices by example how to clean off the old varnish with paint stripper and a yacht's triangular paint scraper. He also showed them how to lay on the new varnish, not thick enough to run, yet not so thin that the wood became sticky and pulled the hairs out of the brush, and laid on in such a methodical way that no 'holidays' would be left innocent of varnish. This course of instruction would be repeated many, many times, and most dry forenoons Reggie, with the new apprentices in tow, could be found somewhere about the midship accommodation, happily working away with scraper and varnish tin.

This suited the Bosun. Chief Mates have to be a bit pedantic, they are paid to be continually peering over the Bosun's shoulder to see how the work is going. Reggie could have been worse than most, he was quite an old woman in the way he kept on about his bridge woodwork, so the Bosun was glad that this left him little time to chase up other work on deck.

His overemphasis on detail was reflected in the stores Reggie ordered for the Deck Department. The owners were never bountiful in their allowance and on principle the Marine Super always made some reductions to every list of stores; it was all part of the game. But Reggie took it very much to heart, and trip after trip he attempted to make his own further reductions. Over the period he had been on the ship the deck stores had been pared well below the sensible minimum level and what little there was had to be carefully hoarded. 'Attractive' items such as paint brushes and light line were stowed in lockers in the Mate's cabin. Cotton waste and paraffin, which the sailors might expect to be freely supplied for cleaning paint off their hands, were almost non-existent and had to be rationed by the Bosun; one wad of waste per man per day and one half pint of paraffin shared amongst them all was all he could manage.

As the Mate was required to spend most of the daylight hours on and around the deck he stood the four to eight watch morning and evening. Thus every day he saw the Sun both rise and set. This was of little aesthetic significance but it did mean that Reggie had the bridge at the only times when both stars and the horizon were suitable for taking sights. By tradition these morning and evening star sights were kept as an independent check on the mid morning and Noon Sun sights of the other mates and the Captain. They were not entered up in the log as it only had space for the official Noon Position, but they were left on laboriously pencilled chits on the chartroom table, twice daily for the oncoming watch. Navigation was just one other aspect of seafaring that was not one of Reggie's strong points. His positions were rarely within five miles of the real track made good, by definition always the one that coincided with the Captain's navigation. Reggie's fallibility was known and tacitly accepted by the other watchkeepers, but after several overcast days without the chance of a sun sight the Captain took to hovering about the bridge with his sextant at the ready at dawn and dusk in case there should be a chance for a snap star sight.

Coming alongside the Mate was in charge of the fo'c'sle, and even if everything went according to plan Reggie was liable to give a virtuoso performance of ineptitude. However as both the Bosun and the Carpenter were part of the fo'c'sle party nothing much went seriously wrong, although there were some pretty close shaves. For some reason the Mate could never quite get the feel of mooring ropes and always slacked them off much too late. When he was on form and the Bosun not alert enough to cover for him, Reggie's fo'c'sle could leave harbour to a veritable fusillade of parting moorings. His best effort was in New Plymouth, when the Bosun had a severe hangover - two parted breast ropes, one spring, a strained insurance wire and a foul hawse!

In port while the Captain handles the ship's business the Mate handles the actual routine of loading and unloading, dealing directly with the stevedores. This was yet another of Reggie's weaker points; his personality was nowhere near tough enough to cope with dock labour, especially the militant wharfies of Australia. On board Reggie's ship it was always the crew who were left to cover the hatches when it rained, whereas other Mates generally succeeded in getting the wharfies to do the job before they sought shelter. There were always far too many stoppages to replace worn cargo gear if the gangs were not on piecework, dangerously few when they were. As Mate Reggie should have regulated this but instead he remained an almost helpless bystander.

For most men such an existence would have been an endless series of frustrations, but to Reggie Baker's gentle soul it was just life. It had always been this way. He was content to drift from voyage to voyage as it was the only work he knew. Even so he did have something else between voyages, he had married late on in life to a formidable West Country widow who farmed in her own right. If Reggie did not have drive of his own Mrs. Baker certainly had enough for two. It was her plan to turn most of her arable into a holiday caravan site with Reggie as the permanent resident plumber, painter and handyman. This meant that Reggie's leaves were a mixture of healthy manual labour, superb farmhouse cooking and relentless nagging to quit the sea for good. Consequently he arrived back off every leave physically fit but so mentally exhausted that he slipped effortlessly back into his accustomed position two or three moves behind the game.

If there was any mystery about Reggie it was why, with all his ineffectualities, he was signed back on as First mate voyage after voyage. Maybe the Captain or the owners had a compassion for gentle misfits they otherwise successfully concealed. Maybe Reggie only appeared ineffectual to us youngsters and could rise to the occasion in a crisis. Neither then seemed a likely option, and they appear even less so in retrospect.

Chapter 27

**John Bateman,
Seaman**

The trees drifted their leaves silently on to the wet grass; the few ducks idly paddling about scarcely rippled the surface with their brown bodies. The only sound to disturb the morning's autumnal stillness was the busy chugging of the blue painted launch towing its string of barges from the dredger to the washing plant at the far end of the gravel pit. Apart from a short break for lunch the boat would be at it from dawn to dusk, steadily plodding its way back and forth, for its owner was on contract work at a fixed rate per load delivered. Most of the local pits had their own boats and boatmen, but some of the smaller ones sub-contracted, which suited the fiercely independent figure at the wheel of the launch far better than the old age pension most men had to rely on at his age.

John Bateman admitted to only seventy of his years, but he must have been well over that, for he had left the sea for the first time before I was born. It was highly likely that he had been too old for his second spell in World War II, but then and for some years thereafter experienced seamen were in such short supply that no one bothered to enquire too closely. Even now the sturdy figure belied its age, although the eyes were perhaps a little dimmed. When they were used for reading, which rarely happened unnecessarily, they now had to be assisted by the steel rimmed spectacles he carried in the pocket of his blue reefer jacket. This jacket he wore winter and summer alike, as he did his seaboots and the navy blue knitted cap with its red bobble. More than his other clothes, this last was his trademark; he almost never removed it. This bobble hat was one of his few vanities, for although he was upright, barrel chested, with a face more creased by weather than by age, and possessed of a bristling grey beard, the top of his head was completely, shiningly bald.

To list John's career was to catalogue nearly half a century of the most varied seagoing experience imaginable. 'Arethusa 1912' was still his proud rejoinder to any query about his early years. In those days the wooden walls of orphanage maintained training ships were a hard prelude to adult life, but the boys thrived under a harshness almost inconceivable in our current affluent society; barefoot throughout the year, freezing cold water and hand scrubbers on the decks every morning, with plain food and not a lot of it either. The schooling was rough and ready too. "I learnt to splice the hard way, our instructor was an ex RN jaunty[1] who was never without a tipped cane under his arm. God help you if you tucked a single spliced end the wrong way." "Still he was a great sailing man." he would conclude, his eyes lighting up with the reminiscence. He had also sailed on a square rigger, but for only one trip as a Deck Boy. In common with most seamen of the twentieth century almost all his time had been spent in steam ships. "Every rating from Deck Boy to Bosun in my Discharge Book, including Quartermaster, and all with a VG Discharge." Nor was this all, for he regarded himself as a tugboat man rather than a deep sea sailor. Whilst an AB on ocean going salvage tugs he had gained an unrivalled knowledge of rigging heavy gear and splicing towing wires. He could discourse on this at great length, not just the simple eye in a two and a half inch spring that marked the limits of most sailors' skills, but of the merits and demerits of many different methods, balancing the time they took against their suitability to the task in hand. One of his proudest possessions was a set of matched spikes[2], each one grooved and sharpened to his own personal requirements.

There was an interlude after the war when John felt it was time to come ashore and settle down. So he took a job as a fitter in a riverside boatyard and such was his skill as an artisan that, despite his advanced age, he rapidly rose to be works foreman, but the requirement for paperwork soon put an end to that. So he became a waterman, picking up a living on the Upper Thames in and around the many boatyards from Teddington to Windsor. He also worked on most of the large civil engineering projects in the area, for in the days before the advent of tower cranes a man who could rig derricks and handle heavy wires was able, within reason, to name his own price. But it was to the river that the retired sailorman always returned. "You get um down by there and when I see um Lord only knows." his wife complained in her rich countrywoman's burr, for she understood the ways of the shepherds of her native Wiltshire far better than those of the sea. How she had ever left her home village for long enough to be courted by John, or alternatively how he had ever strayed far enough from the sea to find her, remained something of an enigma, even to their four grown up offspring.

John's stumpy figure and red bobbled hat became a familiar tow path sight. He was there in all weathers 'Doing a bit of this and a bit of that' from dawn to dusk. One of these ventures was the purchase of an ex-flying boat tender, a stout general purpose twenty five-footer, formerly used to convey passengers and their baggage from Calshot Point to the flying boats bobbing at their moorings in Southampton Water. His first task on getting her back to London was to re-engine her so the

---

1. RN Jaunty - *Nickname for the Master at Arms, the rating heading the ship's police*
2. Spike - *A short piece of metal rod used to open the lay of a rope for splicing*

coastwise journey from the Nab to Sheerness must have been quite an epic. He used to grin and keep a discreet silence whenever it was mentioned, the only facts you could glean were that he made the voyage without calling up the Coastguard, calling out the RNLI or being towed; but when she finally reached Staines and was slipped, her aged engine should quite clearly have chugged out its last some time before. Refitting, caulking and converting her for towing, all in themselves no mean tasks for a boatyard had to be carried out single handed. They took all John's spare time for well over two years, but eventually she took to the water again. She was neither elegant nor particularly speedy, but as befitted her owner well found, workmanlike and well capable of any demands the river could make of her.

It was this boat and its owner that had been sub-contracted by the gravel pit for towing, and on the side for any odd rigging job that cropped up. At first the company were uncertain about employing him, so as a test of his skill they asked him to put an eye splice in a two inch wire. Half an hour later they returned to find John still sitting where they had left him, with a rolled cigarette, half smoked in a gnarled fist, and the wire neatly coiled at his feet, but with not a spliced end in sight. "Sorry," he murmured, his eyes twinkling, "I forgot exactly what you wanted so I just joined him up like for you." So saying he passed up the wire, its two ends so neatly married together in a long splice that only the whippings betrayed the finished off ends. John got the job and also a total immunity from any further question of his ability as a seaman.

This progress over more than half a century, from a bare foot teenager aloft on a square rigger to a grizzled septuagenarian driving a launch on an Isleworth gravel pit has a common theme - the seamanship of the man who proudly referred to himself simply as 'John Bateman; Seaman. Arethusa, 1912.'

Chapter 28

**Mary Duncan,
Hairdresser**

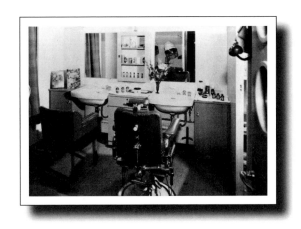

Strictly speaking Mary has no place in this book. Not that she was not in the Merchant Navy. Her Discharge Book proved otherwise; for there on its cover Her Majesty's Government had stamped in bold gold capitals that it was a record of her service at sea. Nor did it refer to her sex in the description, although the scar on her inner left thigh was listed as an 'identifying mark'. It did however carry a passport photograph that was certainly not male, but of a very good looking, much younger Mary than the one we met. She should not really be here because I never actually sailed with her and met her only but once. My only clear recollection of her is a single remark, and that was made by Davy Braid, our Chief Steward, not Mary herself. It is however a vignette that I hold vividly in my mind's eye, and as I am writing of merchant seamen, Mary Duncan shall have her place.

It was unusual for our ship to be in Southampton at all. There among the lofty Queens and the sleeker mail boats our piebald black paint, soot, and rust livery looked totally out of place. I even forget what cargo had brought us there, but it must have carried a premium freight, for berthing costs in a liner port are excessively high in terms of tramp ship economics. However there in Southampton we were.

It was not the Southampton of today with its Civic Centre, shopping malls and acres of high rise office blocks Below Bar; but a city more than a decade after the last all clear still showing the scars of Hitler's bombing. The pub we visited no longer exists; modern Southampton has no place for undistinguished spit and sawdust bars at the dock gates. In such a place on a comfortless November Saturday we met Mary. 'We' were Davy Braid, the Chief Steward; Tommy Carnell, the Fourth Engineer and myself. Mary was a bustling, buxom figure approaching middle age with greying hair. She looked a typical 'Mum' from a suburban street, except that despite her air of respectability she was clearly at home, sitting at her ease in a rather run-down dockside bar. She was on her own, with parcels at her feet and a half pint on the table in front of her. Another rather unusual circumstance, the girls normally found in such places would not have shopping spread at their feet, and most certainly would have been sipping shorts bought by their escorts, not halves they had purchased for themselves.

It was unusual too in that it was Mary who came across to our table, not we to hers. She had, in Davy, recognised the tones of a fellow Scot and so our brief friendship progressed, her halves matching our pints. In the course of the evening we learned something, but not a lot, of Mary's life. Except for Davy, who had been at sea before the war, she had more sea time than any of us. Her first trip had been made when both the Fourth and I were still in short trousers. She had been at sea ever since, but all her working life had been spent between the two ports of Southampton and New York. She was not even familiar with the latter port. Her trade gave her little free time during the quick turn round in America, for every one of the female passengers found a new hair do absolutely vital, and Mary worked in the First Class Coiffure Salon on C Deck.

She had started her sea career already qualified as a hairdresser, for the 'carriage trade' of the Atlantic liners would not accept trainees. Over the years she had advanced as all her seniors, and latterly most of her juniors, had left the sea for more normal feminine occupations. It was not for want of offers either, quite the reverse. Obviously she had been a stunner in her youth and in early middle age she was still not unattractive. Nor was she averse to male company, as her tales of shipboard night life made abundantly clear. To us tramp ship sailors made enforcedly celibate at sea, her tales of inhibitions cast to the wind with the last mooring line were like tales of the exotic east to pimply schoolboys. Unreal, fabulous experiences, but none the less enviable for all that. Mary had stayed at sea simply because this life style suited her better than a humdrum one ashore.

This was about all we learned of Mary over the course of some three hours steady drinking. By this time all of us were a little merry, more as a defence against the cheerless November outside than for any other reason, and in a rather heavy handed way we began to chat Mary up. She gave as good as she got, we were none of us serious, and she knew the rules as well as we did. It was more a training session for us all, Mary included; a means to keep our techniques honed for the future and as a way to pass the otherwise empty hours. In the course of our chatting up we kidded her about her parcels and she in equally good humour informed us that it was her new underwear. I am not sure whether she laid the trap for us, or we for her, but this was the point of no return. Of course we wanted to see it; naturally she at first refused. We countered by lecherously describing its diaphanous imagery, she insisted that it was just ordinary stuff. Our appetites thoroughly whetted we speculated on the material, silk? nylon? lace trimmed? see through? "No." she responded in a Scots lilt, "It is just red flannel!" Declarations of absolute disbelief on our part ended that round. It was now 'put up or shut up time' for Mary. We knew we had won and felt smugly masculine. Mary too saw the game was up and, with a final studied show of coquetry, reluctantly began to loosen the string on her neatly wrapped parcel.

Without batting an eyelid she discarded the last tissue wrapper and solemnly produced the most enveloping pair of red flannel drawers any of us had ever seen. There was complete stunned silence, eventually broken by Davy's soft Highland lilt. "Och, they're very nice, Mary." And that is the one thing by which I remember her, not much maybe, but to my dying day, though places and faces fade I shall be able to hear with enduring freshness Davy's surprised outburst. For that one moment, Mary Duncan, may you sail on in peace.

Chapter 29

**Henry Nicholls,
Carpenter**

He was rated Carpenter, and had served his time ashore in that trade, but in common with every other sea going Chippy, Henry was a general handyman first, and a woodworker second. In sailing ships things had been different, but that had been generations ago. Steel tramp ships had comparatively little wood on which to exercise traditional skills.

A typical shipboard day would start with Henry sounding all the tanks and bilges so that the Engine Room State board could be updated and the Mate have a report in his cabin before breakfast. Then in the forenoon two cracked ports in the midships accommodation needed replacement. After dinner the hatch wedges and battens had to be checked as the forecast was for heavy weather; this at least bore some resemblance to real carpentry, for the wedges were wood and his tool a hammer. Then all the outside door hinges needed oiling, a once weekly task if they were not to seize up in the salt laden air.

Any true wood working was likely to fall into the 'special little job' category of minor repairs to cabin fixtures and other domestic equipment. Ironically the really large carpentering jobs such as fitting wooden shifting boards were not Henry's. Gangs of shore based chippies were employed on this particular task, erecting the giant partitions from floor to ceiling of each hold in order to prevent the cargo from shifting as the grain settled at sea.

The jobs Henry regularly undertook in his role of handyman covered a wide range. Entering port his station was for'ard driving the windlass, if anchoring he would be up there alone with the Mate, if coming alongside he would clutch out the gypsies so that the drum ends would operate separately for handling mooring ropes. Once alongside the Bosun and the sailors would work their way down the deck topping all the derricks, whilst Henry followed them knocking out hatch wedges and collecting them in a sack. Left around the deck they would not only be dangerous underfoot, but they would prove far too useful for a multitude of incidental tasks and,unless safely stowed away in the Chippy's shop, would have vanished overnight. Having done this his next task was to arrange for replenishing the fresh water supply. Both boiler feed and drinking water had to be metered aboard, which nearly always meant working overtime whilst everyone else was ashore, enjoying their first drink for many days. Apart from a single free tot of rum on Saturday evenings, tramp ships were then dry at sea. In a bunkering port this often meant that Henry had no shore leave at all as the ship was only likely to be tied up for a single night.

For this and many other specialist activities the Carpenter was paid more than any other rating on board, and even more than some of the junior officers. Not much more though and, certainly to Henry's way of thinking, not really enough to compensate for loss of the breaks ashore which the others enjoyed at such re-fuelling stops as Honolulu, Curacao, Port Said, Colombo, Singapore and others on the long ocean passages between ports of loading and discharge. For a coal burner going east about there were four such stops between London and Sydney and four more on the homeward run.

When eventually Henry did get ashore he did not go wild. He was a quiet man by nature and rather older than most of the crew. Even his closest shipmate, the Bosun, was a good half a dozen years his junior, whilst the greying Captain for all his quarter century at sea had still been a schoolboy when Henry joined his first ship. He had served throughout the war, mainly on North Atlantic convoys, and yet, surprisingly, even at the height of the U Boat campaign had seen nothing more aggressive than the air raid that devastated the dock area of Liverpool. 'Seen' is not perhaps the correct term, he had certainly heard it, but from inside a concrete street shelter in the town. What he saw was the smoking debris remaining after the raid as he picked his way back on board through the shattered streets, to find his ship almost the only one showing no signs of enemy action despite the smouldering ruins of warehouses all round her. VE and VJ Days for him passed uneventfully at sea without any let up in the daily routine or any chance to join in the universal revels ashore on either occasion.

This was typical of Henry, his luck always seemed to run that way. Because of routine tasks on board he was forever missing out on events going on just the other side of the gangway, or in the shore-side world just below the next horizon. He had, for example, spent only four Christmas Days alongside in all his years at sea, none nearer home than Ceuta in Spanish Morocco, and even then it was a bunkering visit so he did not get ashore. But, he grumbled to himself, he fully intended to make it ashore for his own funeral even if he didn't make for any events before then.

In a vaguely negative way this suited Henry. His solitary life had made him a professional spectator; his pleasure was watching or reading about events rather than taking part. In his off duty time at sea he was a voracious reader and could always be found in his cabin, the glasses he now needed for the smaller print perched with precarious incongruity on his rather dolefully pointed nose. He preferred adventure stories, tales of a lurid fantasy world he would never have wished to live in: 'She Only Wore Blood' and 'Massacre for Money' were typical titles from his library of garishly covered paper backs. They gave him all the excitement he ever craved. On his runs ashore he also preferred to remain a spectator. In every port he bought a local newspaper and scorning the news would turn directly to the entertainment guide. With this he would spend a good half hour deciding the order in which he would see every film that was showing, including those he had seen before. After a stay of more than a week he had usually seen all that really interested him, but he still went, night after night, as much from habit as from an unconscious, though very real need for a break from the close confines of life on board. Whilst his fantasy world at sea was peopled by violence, ashore he much preferred the standard Hollywood domestic situation comedy to the blood and thunder of the film makers' American West. For Henry, a life long bachelor, the stars playing the young matrons were inextricably woven into the background of his dreams of suburban life.

This pattern of existence, established in early youth, remained unchanged. Now in middle age he sometimes wondered what would happen in another dozen years or so. Then he would be approaching sixty five, with nothing saved, for few seamen bothered, or could afford to make such provision. Obviously he could not stay at sea indefinitely, even now he could sense he was slowing up a little, and jobs for retired ships' carpenters were just about non-existent. The problem was unanswerable, and as he was not a worrying man he dismissed it in the only way he knew; two and a half hours viewing the celluloid world he would never enter, would last him to his next night ashore; and at sea a paperback thriller would be sufficient until the next port where there would be new films to see.

Chapter 30

Pete Howard,
Ex-Mate

The wind whipped across the flight deck as the carrier steamed into the breeze at thirty knots. In higher latitudes this might have made the Batman's task a test of endurance, but here under a blazing Mediterranean sun it was a pleasant relief from the steamy heat below decks. As the aircraft approached the round down, the bats were tilted this way and that to indicate the precise changes of attitude required of the pilot until with a final flourish they were crossed. Then with throttles jammed shut the aircraft fell the last few feet with a resounding clang, hooked a wire and came to a dramatic, shuddering stop. With barely a glance behind him to check that the deck was clear and the wires reset Bats marshalled the next in the stream to a landing only fifteen seconds later. And so it would go on, on the hour every hour of daylight as the carrier turned into wind to recover aircraft. In the intervals it was just possible to snatch a quick cigarette or a hasty snack before being piped back to the deck.

It was an exacting task requiring the utmost of skill from a trained pilot, together with a definite unflappableness; for any one of the hundred or so daily landings could become a catastrophe if the Batman made a single error. In the final stages of the approach neither the touch down point nor the wires could be clearly seen from the cockpit, so the landing aircraft were completely dependent on the vital information passed by the bats.

Perhaps an unusual situation for a man holding a First Mates Ticket, but not nearly so rare as you might imagine, for Pete Howard was one of the many Merchant Navy officers lured away by Short Service Aircrew Commissions. Certainly the pay and conditions were better, and the life more glamourous. Maybe there was less security, you were virtually assured unemployment at the end of eight years, but this weighed not at all with the type of young men the Royal Navy wanted as aviators. Pete certainly had no regrets. He had been born and bred to inshore fishing, his father skippered a small boat and Pete's one ambition was to own one himself one day. This he might well manage on the gratuity that the Admiralty would pay him when his commission was completed. He certainly could not have saved sufficient working as a fisherman, nor as a Mate on deep sea ships; he had tried both without success. Meanwhile there were many other advantages. A carrier's wardroom was a very pleasant place to spend off duty hours, a tramp ship's cabin was at best a solitary abode, often of almost Spartan bleakness.

In port a Merchant Navy officer could expect polite indifference at best, at worst a thinly veiled dislike. A Royal Navy officer was usually accepted as a welcome guest by the local population. Merchant seamen never serve ashore, but so far in his Royal Navy service Pete had already spent one tour ashore, during which he met and married his wife. Trixie was a Wren signaller, with whom he now spent at least two month's leave every year; as a Merchant Navy Mate he would have been lucky to squeeze any serious courtship into the odd two or three weeks he could be spared between trips. Now he would have a fair chance of watching his children grow up, something which no one in the Merchant Navy could ever hope to do. Obviously there must have been some advantages to sailing under the Red Ensign, but off hand Pete could not think of any. He was not bitter about this, it was not that anyone consciously made a Mate's berth less attractive than that of a Lieutenant RN, it was just a case of 'Different ships, different long splices.' Also, he reflected wryly, he was using his time to build up enough capital to go back to inshore fishing where the living was far harder and more precarious than anything he would find anywhere else at sea.

It was easy to picture Pete as a fisherman in his native Beccles, close by the Norfolk coast. His stocky figure was one that called out for oilskins and souwester; in fact his wardroom colleagues likened him to the similarly clad gentleman who stared up from the label of every tin of Portuguese sardines. Somehow even the artifices of Gieves, that most famous of naval tailors, never converted his bulging muscular silhouette to the sleek elegant figures of their glossy advertisements. Quite frankly in his mess undress with its bum freezer jacket he looked more like a Sherman tank than a naval officer. His cap too was a distinct affront to any dress regulations ever penned; even when new it managed to acquire a battered air and was worn at a Beatty angle, with a stray lock of hair always showing somewhere around its brim.

It would be pleasant to step forward in time and see Pete actually the owner of the fishing smack of his dreams, but it was a case of 'Man proposes........' He left the Royal Navy at the end of his eight years, but his with family commitments his gratuity had to be spent on providing a proper home to replace the somewhat nomadic existence his wife and children had hitherto suffered. Not only did this reduce his capital to near zero, it also left him with a fairly hefty mortgage, so a reasonably well paid civvy job became his first priority. It was not quite the case of any port in a storm, but the range of jobs for ex-service aircrew was not large. So like many others in the same situation he became a civil air traffic controller. Once again it would be pleasant to record that this proved a satisfying career, but Pete found that sitting in a control tower fronting a battery of radio and radar apparatus had little of the salt tang of the sea about it, and he became restless. He is still in aviation, flying helicopters on commercial contract somewhere in the Middle East. He still looks more like a fisherman than either an ex-Royal Navy officer or an executive pilot, is still restless and still dreams of the fishing boat he may yet own some day.

Chapter 31

**Albert Edward Cockcroft,
Master**

For reasons of their own the owners named all their ships after composers whose names began with B; Bach, Bartok, Brahms and so forth. The ancient Beethoven was no exception to this rule, but under a pall of coal dust alongside the bunkering berth in Birkenhead she had very little in common with her namesake's soaring symphonies. She did not even have much about her to remind one of the Kipling-like sturdiness of vessels so fixed in landsmens' imaginations; she was caked but with filth, not the clean salty rust of the poem. Three weeks in port with all the galley refuse left lying in the alleyways mixed in with the clinker from the donkey boiler had created stinking waist high mounds next to the midship accommodation. Dumping them over the side and hosing down would be the crew's task on leaving port, but until then a layer of coal dust and the smell of rotting refuse would remain the ship's most noticeable features.

Nevertheless, to the diminutive figure stepping from the taxi on the quayside she was home. So also was the neat seaside villa he had left only hours ago. This was because Captain Cockcroft led two distinctly separate lives. One was as the dutiful husband, father and, for the last dozen years, grandfather of 'Holmlea', Seaview Avenue, Rushingford by Sea; the other as 'Master Before God' of the S.S. Beethoven of London. In the former life he was an elderly man who loved pottering around, getting under his wife's feet and fussing over his adored grandchildren. In the latter he was, despite his small stature, clearly a figure to command obedience and respect, especially when he stood stolidly on the wing of the bridge in streaming oilskins at the height of a North Atlantic winter gale.

Now he stood on the quay for a few seconds after paying off the taxi in order to complete the mental transition from one life to the other. Then purposefully squaring his shoulders he began to mount the gangway.

Captain Cockcroft had been at sea for more years than he now cared to remember. As an Apprentice he had sailed on steamships when square riggers were still to be found in most ports, when even the largest passenger liners were coal burners, and gyro compasses were virtually unknown. Now, although he was still at sea, square riggers had completely vanished, and the Beethoven with her coal fired boilers and magnetic compass was herself an anachronism. However she was still seaworthy, capable of earning freight for the owners and, mused the Captain, would last out his sea time before being consigned to the scrap heap.

Usually Masters of ships like the Beethoven were comparative youngsters, given the older ships of the fleet as first commands. Few had the wealth of experience accumulated by Captain Cockcroft. He had been a Master for some time before his career had been interrupted by a U Boat torpedo in 1943. His next two years were the longest single time he had spent ashore since childhood, incarcerated in the middle of Bavaria as a guest of the Third Reich. He spoke little of this, but the experience was one he would not easily forgive or forget. An earnest of this was his knowledge of German, he could read it well and understand its spoken word fluently, but adamantly refused to speak a single syllable of it. After the war he returned to his old company and commanded their crack ships. Among other appointments he was the first Captain of the Wanstead Grange, something perhaps of significance only to merchant seamen. She was the very first British tramp where all the crew lived in cabins amidships, with wooden furnishings for the sailors instead of the tin lockers found in other ships' foc's'les down aft. She even had the unheard of luxury of rest rooms furnished with armchairs for the sailors and firemen!

Some years after this he decided it was time to retire and moved his family from their home in suburban Hull to the seaside. Here with his accustomed energy he devoted himself to growing roses. He was successful and after his first season won the first prize at the annual flower show. However this could not fully compensate for an active life at sea and so after less than two years ashore he once again sought a sea going billet. He found one with little difficulty, for there was a shortage of experienced officers. The Merchant Navy had not fully recovered from its wartime losses and there was a boom in shipping. He neither sought nor was offered a modern ship in a prominent company. The Beethoven like her Master was elderly, but still with a few years service left in her.

Captain Cockcroft had now been in command of her for three years and was quite content to remain in that post. For him the ship had added attractions. Her old fashioned cargo gear and longer more frequent repair periods kept her longer in home ports than newer vessels, thus the Captain was able to spend more time ashore with his family than ever before in his seagoing career.

Leaving harbour, once the ship dropped the pilot, the Captain would slip below to change from his stiff collar and tie to the soft shirt and polo neck he favoured at sea. Then, stuffing the most foul smelling pipe with the strongest tobacco he could find, would return to the bridge puffing out clouds of pungent smoke. He would not leave it again until the Beethoven cleared the Channel, having meals brought up on a tray and snatching a few odd hours sleep on the Chartroom settee. He did not interfere with the Mates' watchkeeping, although he would chat with them, perhaps offering advice to the most junior. In clear weather he would spend most of the time alone on the lee wing; at night he was never in the way, nor did his sleeping form inhibit use of the Chartroom for navigation. He was just there, and if needed in an emergency the few seconds saved by his not being in his cabin below might be vital. Such behaviour was perhaps now an over kill, but in common with many others of his vintage it was a habit he had acquired when sailing in mine infested waters and one which he could not shake off in peace time. In bad weather this was welcomed, his many years in command enabled him to step in just when he was needed and in such a way that he did not make the Mates feel that their competence was in any sense being questioned.

In good weather in open waters he always followed the same routine, joining the Second and Third Mates at about ten o'clock to take a morning sight and again at Noon for a meridian altitude, the three of them then working out the day's run. In between these two visits to the bridge he would call on the Chief Engineer for coffee and a discussion of the ship's day to day running. After dinner at midday the Captain spent the early afternoon with his head down, as did everyone else not on watch. At three the Second Steward would wake him up with a cup of tea after which he would usually stroll down to the Chief Stewards cabin for a quick update on the Providore Department, a rather grandiose shipboard title for the Chief, three Stewards, two Cooks, the Galley Boy and the Ship' Stores. This would take him until past four o'clock and, after allowing the First Mate time to settle into his watch, he would then go up on to the bridge to chat about the work on deck which was the Mate's prime routine off-watch responsibility. This would last him until just before five when he would go below to his cabin and wash ready for supper. The meal started at five prompt and was usually finished by half past but Captain Cockcroft normally sat on chatting. This was a typically courteous gesture to the Third Mate who relieved the First Mate on the bridge from five to five thirty, and who would on most ships have been forced to eat alone surrounded by the debris of the meal, with the Assistant Steward hovering at his shoulder striving to clear away and finish as early as possible.

From six to eight the Captain could be found in his cabin working at the ship's accounts or any other of the seemingly myriad paper chores that beset a Shipmaster. At eight he always put his work to one side and kept himself at instant standby, generally by reading a book until midnight. This was because the Third Mate who kept the eight to twelve was uncertificated and so technically the watch was the Captain's responsibility. His choice of reading was eclectic. He would read anything to hand, but merchant ships only had a very limited choice. Small libraries were sent on board in single packing cases, one each from two charities, the Seamen's Mission and the College of the Sea, a grand total of something less than one hundred books to share among a fifty man crew over a six month voyage. Sometimes Captain Cockcroft felt he should ask the owner if the company could provide some further reading material, but not very often, because he knew that they were unlikely to show interest in aspects of crew welfare that were not required of them by the Merchant Shipping Act.

So he passed his days in contented self confidence for he was generally right about most things connected with seafaring. You had to be so if you were to remain employed as a ship's master for upwards of twenty years; but he did make one error in timing. Neither he nor the ship had quite the mileage left to them that he imagined. He was master of the Beethoven for only four years before he quietly slipped away in his bed at Rushingford by Sea, victim of an unexpected heart attack. As for the ship, the post war boom ended and newer ships than the Beethoven were laid up by the score, but not old coal burners. She only outstayed her old captain by one short voyage before making her last trip under tow to a breaker's yard on Tyneside.

Chapter 32

The Seamens' Missions,
Home from Home

Most large ports had at least one Seamen's Mission, many had three; Church of England, Roman Catholic and Non-Conformist. The C of E 'Flying Ashbag' was by far the largest, its nickname derived from its formal title, 'The Flying Angel Missions to Seamen' and from the figure of a flying angel with a trumpet emblazoned on its flag. The seamen who frequented the missions were labelled as 'Mission Bums' by their shipmates, but even these latter were not averse to using the missions as social clubs when they were broke, or as often happened in Australia in the fifties, when there was a long drawn out strike that repercussed on shipping and breweries so that ships stayed in port and pubs ran out of beer.

The missions had a fairly standard programme. They were open every afternoon and evening; ran two dances a week: had table tennis, billiards and cribbage on the go every night; and on Sunday they ran a fairly relaxed regime of church services. Apart from Sunday the only attempt at religion was the Epilogue at the end of the day's activity, a very simple service taking no more than ten minutes: many seamen stayed out of politeness to the Missioners, but many more stayed at those missions where the padre was wily enough to delay tea and tab nabs[1] until after the Epilogue. Maybe the Missions did not make many converts, but they provided a real service that could be counted upon by any lonely merchant seaman, as did no one else.

The 'Mission Bums' typically came in three age groups, the very young, the middle aged and the elderly. As a tribute to the Missions I will try to describe one from each group; Tom, Dick and Harry.

Tom

Tom was a 'nice young man' from an inner city, with no family background of seafaring. His father had been a bus driver all his life and instilled in young Tom the need for a steady job and loyalty to one's employer - he had been employed on the

---

1. Tab nabs - *collective term for scones, buns or cakes*

local corporation buses all his life and still dreamt of a final promotion to inspector. Tom accepted this but still yearned for adventure, so he went to sea, first as a Deck Boy and worked his way steadily towards Ordinary Seaman staying the while on his first ship.

He was by far the longest serving member of her crew and regarded himself as a 'company man'. At Number 9 Acacia Avenue there was a corner of the lounge that housed Tom's souvenir display, photographs of the ship in several ports of the world, photographs of Tom in these ports or on board, ebony elephants from Colombo, butterfly wing trays from Rio. All the usual souvenirs, the whole ranged against a backcloth of red bunting, a white diamond at its centre embossed with a black lion, the company's house flag, carefully washed and ironed and not a bit like the sooty, frayed rag we generally flew at the mainmast.

In foreign ports Tom would be found in the Mission most nights. If there was anyone to give him a game he would play table tennis with more enthusiasm than skill, but it was the dances that really attracted him. The hostesses were recruited from the local church congregations, they were generally good looking but all many years older than the deck boy. However nothing daunted Tom promptly fell in love with the most attractive one, and was her avid ballroom dancing pupil. But as the ship only stayed in port four or five days at most he was falling in and out of love too often and too rapidly, either to experience any pangs at parting, or to become a proficient dancer.

Dick

An older version of Tom, Dick was a married man with a family, no longer young enough to want a casual female companion to be anything more than a friendly presence in the armchair opposite. For him the Missions provided the armchair that was lacking on board, steel frame stacking chairs were all the company provided for seamens' cabins and mess rooms. The companionship was provided by the same team of young ladies who danced with Tom and his like; to Dick they would chat about home, theirs or his, and would show genuine interest in his family photographs. Moreover they could make a fair old cup of tea, and most were the very devils at cribbage. It was also great fun to teach them the complexities of billiards and snooker. The ladies themselves displayed supremely deceptive ineptitude in this; they mishandled cues and were shown how to do it properly night after night, week in week out. They always progressed steadily to their tutors' satisfaction, but as soon as one ship left they were back to hopeless tyros for the next crew to teach all over again.

An evening in the Mission was like visiting a distant relative for tea at home. There was genuine companionship, easy familiarity, a warm hearth and even the lonely walk back afterwards was reminiscent of the one taken to catch the last bus home. The mission was also a very pleasant place to pop in to on the way back from the pictures, it prolonged the evening away from the emptiness of shipboard life for a family man.

Harry

Harry was not an old soldier, he was one of the many ex-Merchant Seamen in the seaport town. He nursed his half pint in the British Legion Bar alongside, but apart from, the other veterans who all wore their ribbons and regimental badges with pride as often as propriety allowed. He was probably entitled to as many ribbons as most and the Merchant Navy certainly had a badge but Harry had never been on for such display. It was just his scene, this anonymity in a crowd in a vaguely institutionalised atmosphere. After the only half pint he could afford he would wonder back through the darkened streets to the hostel where he had a lonely room among others who led similar solitary existences.

This took care of Harry's day from early evening through bar opening hours and up to breakfast in the hostel canteen, but left a great gap after the '0930 Vacate Rooms' rule of the hostel. The period until lunch could be filled by sitting on a park bench if it was sunny, or reading newspapers in the public library if the weather was inclement. It was perhaps this last that kept Harry a level above the down and outs who slept rough. To be acceptable to the librarians you had to be fairly neat, clean and odourless.

However this was just to fill in time before lunch. Then the 'Flying Angel' opened its doors. Inside were free cups of tea and snacks at very reasonable prices. Here were also cosy armchairs, warmth and above all companionship from cronies like himself, from the Missioner bustling in and out and sometimes from the support hostess manning the tea bar. Harry did not often stay for the evenings entertainment of dances or cribbage; he neither danced nor played cards and preferred to sink an evening beer, but the Mission was strictly teetotal. Even so the Mission still provided one of the four cornerstones of Harry's daily round so many years after he had left the sea, nor did it ask anything in return.

Chapter 33

Tim Claymore,
Senior Apprentice

"Do you think you're on your Daddy's yacht?" That standard Merchant Navy catchphrase was never heard on board the S.S. Sunrise, at least not within Tim's earshot. Tim was the Senior Apprentice and a third tripper when I first met him, but that was not the full story.

"Don't give him any special treatment." was the instruction, and the Captain had followed it to the letter. Tim most certainly had no more privileges than would have been accorded to any other shipowner's son who happened to be a member of the crew.

Under the terms of their indentures Apprentices were supposed to be taught the skills and duties of a ship's officer. But traditionally on tramps, at least their first three, if not the whole four years of their time was spent working on deck with chipping hammer and sugee wad (thus saving the owner the cost of employing another hand at a full man's rate of pay). Tim had worked on the deck for one trip only, just to get the feel of the task. At the end of that trip he was put on watch with the Second Mate to learn navigation, something that happened but rarely, and then only to Apprentices who had completed their four years and were going home to sit for their tickets. Tim genuinely did not want special treatment, he would have been much happier working about the deck with the rest of the crowd, and he could well have been right. With his background and education he needed less time than most Apprentices to acquire the academic disciplines of navigation, but correspondingly more to master the manual skills of the seaman. However there was not a great deal he could do about it, for at sea the Captain's word was law, even when it came to offering privileges to shipowners.

111

This difference in treatment could not pass unnoticed. It was a tribute to Tim's personality that it was not resented, even by his cabin mate. Indeed the reverse was true, the Junior Apprentice obviously relished the reflected glory of being on first name terms with the owner's son. The Second Mate also approved of the situation. It was not that he needed the assistance, for like all watchkeeping Mates he stretched out his navigational duties to the full in order to keep himself occupied and alert during the long empty watches. The four hour twice daily vigil, seven days a week, with the helmsman as his only human contact, made Tim's presence a most welcome change. Tim was intelligent and took a lively interest in everything connected with ships and the sea; whilst for the Second Mate, a born teacher, it had been a long time since he had been able to demonstrate his knowledge of navigation from First Principles to Marc St. Hilaire, or been forced to defend some of his entrenched navigational peccadilloes to the questioning of a keen young mind. The two of them could often be found on the bridge wing in the early morning discussing the relative merits of different ways of laying out the Day's Work. The Second Mate was very proud of the minute figures pencilled in his Sight Book, always in exactly the same order so that no explanatory headings were needed, and so spaced that one page served several days. Tim felt that each item should be clearly labelled and each day started on a fresh page so that anyone could clearly read and understand the workings. This was one personal trait that the Second could not logically defend, beyond saying that it had always been so; neither he nor his listener suspected it was a centuries old tradition inherited from the first Elizabeth's Merchant Venturers, to whom charts and navigational records were closely guarded commercial secrets.

Tim was thoroughly at home on board. Had circumstances been different he would have gladly exchanged his pre-destined board room chair in Leadenhall Street for the more open life at sea, but he knew it could not be so. For Tim these four years were an oasis between boyhood and manhood, an interregnum between the arid discipline of a public school and the rat race mores of the City. He intended to enjoy them to the full, and he did, to the enhancement of his shipboard reputation. In some of their wilder daydreams his shipmates imagined themselves met on the quayside by exotic true blondes in fast sports cars; in real life they hired battered taxis to rendezvous with the overblown bottle dyed variety. Now here amongst them was someone who had actually made it - or as the Cook remarked with his dry cynicism - had had it made for him. Always a handful of the crew were leaning over the rail, erotic fantasy masquerading as casual interest, whenever the latest girl friend called for the Senior Apprentice. Sometimes she had on a revealingly short tennis skirt, and once one even wore a bikini! Tim was conscious of this and for his first two trips had tried to share his good fortune. He could well remember some embarrassing parties when having introduced his shipmates to the younger social set he had found himself to be the only possible point of mutual contact. So now he played up to his gallery, but did not attempt to invite them to join in. He had learned from experience that while the crew enjoyed looking at the streamlined upper crust beauties, they much preferred to mix with the more available, less expensive girls that were to be found in and around the dockside area. Often after an expensive evening of polite, inane social banter Tim felt he knew how the crew felt; at least the girls they met shared the seaman's common interests; booze first, sex after.

But life in port was not all beer and skittles, for as well as working on the ship Tim had to learn about its business. This was something spared other Apprentices, and often they would have time off, with shore leave, whilst Tim was left on board working on the ship's papers under the tutelage of the Captain or the Mate. He could also find himself ashore accepting the Agent's official hospitality, a rather boring process at the best of times, and usually the lot of the Captain, who in this case was only too pleased to be able to share the load and thus gain a few free evenings for himself.

In all Tim made five trips on the Sunrise, the first four were rather uneventful, but the last was unique in the ship's history. No one was really surprised when he was promoted acting Third Mate; but they were very surprised when his mother took passage with the ship, using the otherwise empty pilot's cabin. The crew were only mildly surprised when the gorgeous honey blonde of the last trip (she of the bikini) was waiting on the quayside when the ship docked in Sydney; only slightly less surprised when she followed the ship down to Melbourne; but certainly very surprised when as the new Mrs. Tim Claymore she embarked at Fremantle, our last Australian port of call. The purpose of mother's trip was then apparent. Perhaps a shared bunk in a tramp ship's hospital is not an ideal place for a honeymoon, perhaps having her groom on a bridge watch from eight to twelve each morning and evening is not the perfect way for a bride to spend it. But as one envious crewman remarked, "Maybe not, but what a hell of a way to avoid the Channels."

Chapter 34

Wtodak Neckrwynski,
Second Mate

Wtodak Neckrwynski was an unusual man to find on a British ship; even his name had to be shortened to Willie Neski because no one on board could either spell or pronounce it in its correct form. Willie had been born into the landed Polish gentry, but by courtesy of the Third Reich he finished World War II without land, money or family, serving as an officer on a destroyer. Upon demobilisation he chose, wisely, to stay in Britain and tried a variety of jobs whilst living among the Polish emigre community at the Marble Arch end of the Edgware Road. It was during this period that he met his wife. After his marriage he became a moderately wealthy businessman and moved from London to purchase a house in Cheltenham, but he could not settle, the call of the sea was too strong. So Willie returned to the only life in which he was happy, the sea. Thus in early middle age Wtodak Neckrwynski, Lieutenant Commander, Free Polish Navy, became Willie Neski, Second Mate of a British tramp ship.

He was not a large man, but he was an impressive figure. He was the only officer on board to appear on watch in a complete uniform with a collar and tie: the other Mates being quite content to settle for grey flannel trousers, uniform jackets and open necked coloured sports shirts. Willie was also a physical fitness fanatic. It was well known that any thumps and grunts from the wing of the bridge during the graveyard watch, from midnight to 0400, would be the Second Mate doing his twenty chin ups on the awning spars. These were only part of Willie's nightly ritual; he also did thirty press ups and a complete sequence of the strengthening exercises as prescribed in the correspondence courses of Mr. Charles Atlas. The crew firmly believed that, in addition, he was a judo Black Belt. He was not, but he was well aware of the popular belief and did nothing to discourage it. For all his love of the sea Willie Neski was not serving on a tramp ship from choice. On a passenger liner his Second Mate's ticket would have only secured him a junior watchkeeping billet, requiring him to serve a longer time before he could sit for his Mate's and Master's tickets. As this more extended route to command would not have suited Willie, tramp ships it had to be. In any case, as most of his off duty hours were spent studying, the comparative squalor of his cabin when compared to his semi in Cheltenham did not rankle unduly.

It was not the professional aspects that gave him trouble, for he was a seaman to his fingertips, rather it was the technical English he was required to master. Typical of this was the Rule of the Road which all aspirants must learn by heart. Article 24 (as it then was) states categorically that '...notwithstanding anything contained in these rules every vessel overtaking any other vessel shall keep clear of the overtaken vessel and no subsequent alteration of course shall relieve her of that responsibility until she is finally passed and clear.' In desperation Willie, when swotting for his Second's ticket, had scored 'What a bloody language.' in letters that nearly cut through the pages of his Nicholl's Seamanship. He was finding the same to be true of the legal verbiage he now needed to study for his next examination.

The English language was not all exasperation, it provided humour both for Willie and for those who suffered his occasionally fractured English. There was the wonderful day he discovered commercial radio. For weeks thereafter he would creep up behind you and starting in a low gravelly voice would rise to a final roaring crescendo chanting ' A - S - P - R - O, Aspro.' before dissolving into fits of laughter. His normal conversation came in short guttural bursts, rather like machine gun fire, and was almost totally innocent of articles and conjunctions. He often came out with odd statements that became the ship's catchphrase for weeks afterwards. Of these his most memorable was that used to express surprise - "The next thing I see; bare bottom." The midship accommodation had only one hand basin with running water in its single bathroom cum toilet shared by the three Mates, two Apprentices, Sparks and the Chief Steward. By common consent the door was never locked whilst the basin or the bath was in use, and it was accepted that a knock on the door would elicit an automatic invitation to enter no matter in what state of nudity the bather might be. The bridge had no domestic fittings whatsoever so any watchkeeper caught short had to stick it out or make a mad dash two decks below. One Atlantic winter's night with a full gale blowing, Willie was enjoying a leisurely bath before turning in when suddenly, without the customary knock, the door burst open and in rushed the Mate scattering gloves, duffel coat, scarves and oilskins in an advanced state of emergency; and as Willie said, "Next thing I see; bare bottom."

Polish as a language is redolent with expletives, far ahead of seamen's English which has virtually only one adjective, bloody, and just the one four letter swear word, that is unless you count as a separate word its Liverpudlian rendering of 'fock'. In Polish you can swear, blaspheme and even bestialise. 'Shagref', blood of a dog was perhaps Willie's favourite, it was even his nickname down aft, but 'Crucifix' came a close second, and there were countless other normal swear words besides.

It was in the winter gales that the Second mate really came into his own. Something in his nature responded in harmony with a ship rolling her insides out in a freezing force eight gale. He always maintained with gusto, "Rolling deck is best exercise for liver." but never offered further explanation. He also possessed a lined sheepskin leather siren suit so thick that his short broad frame appeared almost spherical. From the depths of this garment he was fond of issuing in a sepulchral tone another pearl of wisdom, "First duty of officer of watch is to keep warm."

In port Willie seemed lost: being neither a heavy drinker nor a womaniser he had little or no common shore going interests with anyone else on board. Often he went for walks, always alone, striding off arms swinging, one hundred and twenty paces to the minute as if on a route march. Before these walks he would study the local area with care, planning his journey to take in any places of interest, although I fear that he found few within walking distance of the berths used by British tramp ships. Very occasionally this routine became too soul destroying even for Willie and he would retire to his cabin with a bottle of whisky, only to emerge twenty four hours later with bloodshot eyes and a vile temper that lasted him until the ship was at sea again.

Willie Neski was a character you could respect, but would never get to know. Although he appeared entirely self contained it is more than possible that he was at times desperately lonely; but driven by some inner compulsion he forged onward alone until, eventually, he obtained the command for which he had worked so hard and long.

Chapter 35

**Denta and Chinta,
Deck Cargo**

Tramp ships had many distinctive smells. Some were permanent, such as the mixture of oil and steam that gave a peculiarly sweetish smell to the engine room; some were periodic, for example the aroma of burnt greaseproof paper that accompanied the daily baking, and the less pleasant once a trip stench of fuel oil painted over the decks to lift rust. There were others that may be classed as occasional, and were mostly allied to the cargo. Of these the least acceptable must have been that of grain rotting in the bilges after washing out the holds.

Perhaps the most pleasant I remember was when we carried Denta and Chinta as deck cargo, two racehorses in loose boxes alongside Number Four hatch. In order to keep them fed, warm and happy we had to fill a complete side pocket down to the tween deck with bales of hay and straw. This gave off a fresh countryside smell whenever the weather was good enough to lift the hatch covers. You could sit in the sun on Number Three, shut your eyes, breathe deeply and almost imagine yourself back at home in summer. If you really let your imagination run riot you could strain your ears listening for the hum of bees.

Had it been a few years later such valuable bloodstock would have travelled by air. Even then it was most unusual for livestock to make the long journey from UK to Australia on a ten knot tramp. Generally they were sent on the faster cargo liners and mail boats. It could be that we offered the cheapest transport, for although Denta and Chinta were bloodstock racehorses, they were not successful enough to have been previously known to the several followers of form we had on board. However there they were in two specially constructed wooden stables with space sufficient to turn round or lie down, but with no possibility of exercise. Most of the time they just stood quietly with their heads protruding out over the half doors if it was fine, but withdrawn well inside the straw when it was not; with any rolling at all they were forced to take one or two shuffling steps backwards or forwards to accommodate to the ship's movement. In really rough weather when the rolling and pitching imparted an irregular jerking motion to the decks which could have endangered their legs they were wedged upright by puddening spars, specially fitted wooden beams swathed in straw and burlap, looking for all the world like the lagging around a large water pipe. This left the horses no liberty at all for movement, but at least their legs were safeguarded from injury.

They had to be cleaned, fed and watered daily. This task was officially assigned by the Master to the Mate, who further assigned it down to the Apprentices, who being the most junior bodies on board could not delegate it to anyone else and so had to take on this additional chore. It was not an unpaid task; the care of the horses had been allowed for in the freight the company levied. The Mate could be sure of a satisfactory, though unofficial recompense for his pains if his charges were delivered in a fit and healthy condition. Cynically the Apprentices were pretty certain that all of the kicks and none of the halfpence would come their way, and they were not mistaken.

So for five weeks at 0830 every morning one of the aspiring officers would convert himself into a stable boy, armed with bucket, broom, shovel and, if the weather was fine, a hose pipe as well. The other Apprentice would measure out and mix the feed as laid down in the instructions supplied by the shipper, refill two nose bags with hay and supply the horses with their first feed of the day. They were fed again in the evening, and also given a brush down, not perhaps to the glossy standard of the show ring, but enough to remove matted straw from their coats and any accumulations of filth from their hooves and hindquarters. The horses were supposed to be combed as well, but the two Apprentices were not country bred and the two racehorses were highly strung. The first attempt at combing was the last, for when the comb first pulled at some knotted hair Chinta shied and both apprentices were out of the horse box almost before the hooves touched the ground. The curry comb, left where it fell on the stable floor, was quietly swept up and dumped overside at the next mucking out session. As tramp ships, for all their variety of stores, do not carry spare gear for grooming horses the exercise could not be repeated. To judge from their condition on reaching Sydney, a month's lay off from combing makes little difference to a well fed, well brushed but uncombed horse, at least not in the eyes of a seaman.

As well as providing a novel task for the two junior officers, a pleasant new shipboard smell and, for the Mate at least, the prospect of a handsome windfall, the horses fulfilled another service; they became a focal point. Normally the crew have little to interest them off duty save reading and conversation. A walk round the deck turns up nothing they have not seen many hundreds of times before, and the sea, despite centuries of lyrical prose, still has a very restricted scenic value for the average seaman. The racehorses were different. Here were two creatures that could be talked to, watched, even fondled maybe and, like the ship's cat, could be certain of an audience of off duty sailors and firemen. The crew discovered that Chinta, a handsome chestnut, could have her neck and nose scratched and tickled, but that it was courting disaster ever to allow your fingers to stray away from the white blaze on Denta's forehead. For the crew they had an advantage over the ship's cat, for that supercilious independent soul would stalk off after only a very few minutes of social intercourse.

The crowd[1], all big city boys, learned a fair bit about the dietary preference of racehorses. It was inevitable that early on in the voyage they would be offered unlighted cigarettes and raw potatoes; the former were acceptable only to Denta, but only occasionally and then only if they were not tipped. Raw potatoes were rejected with a scornful toss of the head by both horses alike. It must have been in the third week that the Peggy tried them with cornflakes, milk and sugar in an old sugee bucket. It was this, rather than their laid down staples of oats and bran mash, to which their increased girth and glossy coats at the voyage end must be attributed. It was perhaps lucky for the horses' health that the Chief Steward was not over generous with the crew's provisions and kept them very much to scale.

The crowd became so attached to the two horses that some even bothered to find out where they were being sent when they were off-loaded at Sydney. When they learnt that the horses would be rested for a couple of days in a paddock within easy reach of a tram route they decided to visit en- masse. However such is the way of seamen that although many set out only a few got as far as the tram stop and none arrived at the horse paddock, all having been diverted into bars en- route. So, despite all the good intentions, the two heads still patiently protruding from their loose boxes as they were swung up over the rail was the last any of us saw of our deck cargo, and once again the ship's cat could reign alone and disdainfully supreme.

---

1. Crowd - *The deck sailors, sometimes including the firemen, but never the Mates and Engineers*

Chapter 36

Joan Macavity,
Mate's Wife

I am sure Tony will not mind me writing about his mother; nor I am sure will she. Neither Tony nor his mother have ever been to sea, although both have strong family connections. One is the son, the other the widow, of a seaman. They do not appear in the telephone book as Macavity, but I am sure the ghost of T.S. Eliot will forgive my plagiarism.

Tony has a newish bungalow in an outer suburb of Sydney, built on the hillside with distant views of the bush on one hand and a quiet arm of the harbour on the other. It was here in Australia that I met Mrs. Macavity, a bustling, buxom sixty-five year old, still with an unmistakable North Country accent despite her many years down under. Originally she had come to help with their first baby, for Tony's wife Jenny's parents were both dead. Then as Tony was her only living relative, and as England was all of twelve thousand miles away, she had just stayed on. Fortunately she and Jenny got on, there was nothing of the music hall Mother-in-Law about their relationship; in fact Tony often jokingly asked just whose mother she thought she was.

Standing on the bungalow verandah, making tweeting noises to attract kookaburras down to food scraps, she looked like any one of thousands of grandmothers the world over. There was nothing at all to suggest any connection with ships or the sea until she spoke of Tony's boyhood. All the usual childhood exploits were catalogued, but they featured one parent only and most ended "Of course, my husband was at sea at the time." It was quite easy to discover that she, like many other Merchant Navy wives, had had to bring up her family almost entirely on her own. It also became apparent that after the first seven years there was no longer any mention of a father at sea. Mrs. Macavity was by no means exceptional. She had been married for eight years, and as I subsequently found out, in that time she and her husband had been together only thirteen weeks in all; two of them as a honeymoon, the rest in odd snatched weekends. In pre-war days seamen were thankful enough to have a berth at all, leave and family had to give way to the sheer necessity of breadwinning. Then came the War, and one of the earliest U Boat attacks had carried her husband to the bottom. That had been thirty years ago and now her son grown up, she could talk of it without emotion; so long ago - or was it such a brief relationship - that she now referred to him only as "my husband" or as "Tony's father", never by a christian name. Yes, it had not been easy. Young people today, and here she looked lovingly at Tony and Jenny, did not realise how lucky they were to be able to bring up a family together.

This conversation was forgotten for many long years. We were in the middle of a seaman's strike, unusually pointless and needlessly damaging to an already shaky economy. My bowler hatted travelling companion on the Drain[1] raged from beneath his paper, "Bloody seamen, why the hell should they be allowed to hold the whole country to ransom for weeks on end." 'Why, indeed' I was about to growl in reply. Then, ironically, his words triggered memories of Mrs. Macavity and her thirteen weeks; I kept silent.

1. Drain - *A nickname for the Waterloo and City line of the London Underground railway system*

Chapter 37

**John Wales,
Radio Operator**

The age of technology had completely ignored the S.S. Porlock Weir. Although of immediate post-war build she was a coal burner, and had neither gyro compass nor radar, yet in one respect her equipment was the equal of any other cargo vessel of her size. This was her radio room where the equipment, supplied and operated by the Marconi Company, conformed to their standards, not minimalised to statutory requirements grudgingly provided by the ship's owners. Here was the Auto Alarm, listening out twenty-four hours a day on 500kcs the International Distress frequency, ready to set bells clanging in Spark's cabin should any ship within hundreds of miles send out four long dashes. Here also was the latest commercial HF Direction Finder, installed because the Board of Trade decreed one should be fitted in every UK registered vessel of over 500 tons, although as a navigational aid it did not really earn its keep, and had in fact been used only once in the past eighteen months. In a larger ship the inventory would have gone on to list other modern radio aids, but not on the Porlock Weir. That is except for the only other transmitter on board; the one kept for Number Three Lifeboat sat in the corner with its battery on constant trickle charge.

Here, if anywhere on board, you would expect to find a technician, and be least likely to discover a countryman, but John Wales was most definitely one of the latter. He did not have the look of a farmer, he was far too slightly built, but he could only have come from one of the rolling English shires. It was difficult to quantify this impression, but it was nevertheless true, for John Wales had been born and bred in the parsonage of a small Gloucestershire village where his father had held the living for over thirty years. The natural reticence of a countryman also helped to highlight his uniqueness on board. Of all the members of the crew only, the Sparks was not on the owner's payroll. His employer was the Marconi Company, and he had to make a direct draught on them for anything over the twenty-five per cent of his salary which they paid directly into his account on board. He was also the only person on board who signed on as an officer. The Captain signed on as Master, the watchkeepers as

Mates or Engineers; Sparks signed as Radio Officer. All this tended to set him apart from the rest of the ship's company, and on short trips any Sparks would have to be something of an extrovert to develop more than a passing acquaintance with his shipmates before being posted to another vessel. This happened frequently because the Marconi Company saw to it that their employees were given the full leave to which they were due; the remainder of the afterguard could rarely take their full leave entitlement before the ship sailed again. An extrovert John certainly was not, and as the Porlock Weir was on a time charter requiring short three month trips to the Mediterranean he made few firm friends during his time on board.

His hours of watch were no help either. As the only radio operator on board he kept four watches daily. Two on, two off, from 0800 to 2000 on zone time, which meant that, no matter what the longitude, all ships in the same part of the ocean kept the same watches throughout the daylight hours. As all the other watchkeepers were four on, eight off, on local time no one was ever quite sure whether Sparks was on watch or not; or whether his current watch cycle allowed him to eat in the saloon instead of off a tray in his cabin cum office. Having meals brought to him on a tray was a privilege he shared only with the Captain, but whereas the latter exercised it for comfort or convenience, Sparks had to use it because his two hour watch sequence often made it impossible for him to fit in with regular meal times. A privilege he did not share with the captain was the use of the boatdeck between the bridge and the weather deck, although both the Captain's suite and the Sparks cabin opened directly on to this deck it was definitely the Captain's preserve, only encroached by others on their way to the bridge, with Sparks the one exception. He could use it to go to and from the bathroom or saloon on the weather deck or to the gangway, but only because there was no other way by which he could reach them.

This enforced semi-solitude did not bother John unduly, for paradoxically he was the only man on board in daily contact with a wide circle of friends. He had only to place his earphones on his head and at once he was in contact with other Radio Officers, both in shore stations and afloat. Reporting on watch on 'Five Ton[1]' before reverting to the normal watchkeeping frequency was equivalent to leaving a calling card on every one of a hundred or more ships, many of whom would call up for a chat whenever their more important traffic fell off. John was a lively participant in these sessions, for in the same way that many shy people find it easy to express themselves freely and at length on paper, so Sparks found his voice through his fingers and a morse key. Their talk was mainly shop, with just the odd word stuck in on the end of routine transmissions, this because it was neither permissible to clutter watch keeping channels with unnecessary traffic, nor to change frequency for a private chat. So generations of operators had built up a nigh on unintelligible shorthand in almost impossibly high speed morse with complete words and phrases reduced to one or two symbols. After a while the various operators could recognise

1. 'Five Ton' - *Informal reference to the 500kcs International Distress frequency*

one another by their sending techniques alone, and call signs became almost superfluous. John believed you could read their characters by this method as well. For example, the flourish of the Royston Grange indicated a swashbuckling womaniser was on the key, whilst the precise clipped dots and dashes of the Hazelwood were obviously from a middle aged pecksniff. In fact Royston Grange was a disgruntled, dyspeptic whose flourish was a sign of his utter contempt for the whole system and Hazelwood a first tripper whose precision was the result of a fierce determination to make no mistakes. However as the two ships were bound for the Atlantic and Pacific respectively, John Wales, Mediterranean bound, would not on this occasion discover he had been mistaken. Doubtless other operators built up pictures of John as they read his morse, probably they too were wrong, for they were unlikely to visualise the shy son of a country parson from the crisp aggressive thumping he gave his key.

So at sea Sparks pursued his solitary existence shared between his cabin and the adjoining radio room. He rarely appeared on deck, except to use the ladders down to the saloon and bathroom, or up to the bridge to deliver the twice daily weather forecasts. Like many countrymen he did not feel the city dwellers' urge to seek fresh air, so while he probably had more spare time in the daylight hours, he alone of all the younger men did not bother to acquire a suntan. Thus while everyone else turned a healthy biscuit colour in the first few weeks John stubbornly retained his indoor pallor.

In port he was still the odd man out. Once the first rope went ashore he closed down his watches until the ship left. He could not have continued even had he wanted to, for the main aerial stretched from his office across Number Three hatch to the triatic stay, and so had to come down whenever the derricks were topped for working cargo. So while everyone else on board worked full time in port, Sparks had only the very minimum of routine maintenance, probably no more than two hours at the most in any port. After that the time was entirely his own, to go ashore or to remain in his cabin at will. It was in port that he caught up with all the reading, sleeping and dhobying that his watch schedule made him miss at sea. He was the only member of the crew to go ashore bedecked with cameras on sight seeing tours; for the others free time was too precious to be wasted on just looking at things. In the evenings John still had plenty of time to go ashore with the rest of us, but he rarely did. It was not that he was teetotal or a woman hater, but the orgiastic beer swilling of a Merchant Navy run ashore in a Mediterranean port was as far different from a quiet pint in a Cotswold pub, as were the attentions of the dockside girls from those of the buxom farmer's daughter he was planning to marry. So with a typical countryman's patience John was content to bide his time until pay off day, after which he could enjoy a spell of real home life before being recalled to his monastic existence on board another ship that would for him be almost identical to the Porlock Weir.

Chapter 38

Frank Doherty,
Fireman

"Warts and all." was Cromwell's edict; ugly he might have been, but as Lord Protector he could be sure that the painter would emphasise any good features as well. No such magnanimous gesture would have availed Frank Doherty, for he had neither influence, nor in all honestly any good features to be emphasised. He was of the race loosely termed Liverpool Irish, a product of one of the gangs of children which used to roam the back streets of the Scotland Road area. Sometimes a minority of these gangs might be found in school but more often than not Frank Doherty and his cronies would be truants, ranging light fingeredly over shopfronts and dockside.

Lunchtime would always find them hovering around the Chippie for a 'Cod and six penn'orth.' with the generous scoop of the mushy peas that were then never found in any fish and chip shop south of Bootle. Evenings they would be kicking and scuffing around cinemas or youth clubs for they were as yet too young to be admitted to the adult society of the pubs; this not from any parental solicitude but because kids just would not have enough money to stand their rounds until they dropped out of school at around fourteen or so. Most of these gangs came to the notice of the police before their members drifted into jobs in the factories, on the docks or to sea. Some might overstep the permitted bounds and finish up on the wrong side of the law, but in the main they only qualified for that little extra degree of vigilance that made the police their sworn enemies for life. There was of course no question of any of them getting good jobs, their schooling had been totally inadequate for that, and anyway such jobs did not exist in or around the Scotland Road. So Frank Doherty went to sea as a Fireman Trimmer with no real interest in anything much at all, a victim in equal parts of environment, lack of opportunity and a paucity of natural ability.

In fiction this would be the point where, despite all setbacks a heart of gold would be revealed. But alas this is a true story, its only fictional element being the Fireman's real name, which bears no semblance at all to Frank Doherty. With his upbringing and intelligence he would have been a most remarkable man had he turned out well and that he certainly was not. Neither big enough nor powerful enough to become a real hard case he was just a thoroughly unpleasant character. Less than medium height, balding and with no front teeth he was no oil painting. His tastes ran to booze and women, both of them the cheapest he could find. His idea of a night out was to get sickeningly drunk in a brothel before satisfying his crude animal passions. It was not solely because a better class of woman would have nothing to do with him, for plenty of worse cases than Frank Doherty have been saved by the love of a good woman. Frank just was not interested in anything higher than his chosen low standards.

As the years wore on even these women ceased to satisfy him and, although they plied their trade with almost no sentiment, even they could not altogether conceal their repugnance at his behaviour and tastes. So Frank was forced to look elsewhere and in so doing stepped well beyond the pale of the most tolerant of societies. The crew to a man were wary of the fireman, he appeared to them as trouble with a capital T, and whilst not exactly ostracised he was manifestly not welcome in their company. He was forced to go ashore and return on his own; the rest of the crowd seemed to melt away when he got out his shore going gear.

Nearly always he would return truculent, very drunk and spoiling for a fight. But on this one particular night his unusually quiet behaviour should have indicated that he had some scheme in mind. It was around midnight when he entered the midships accommodation and knocked on the Apprentices' cabin door. His story was barely coherent, for his speech, never clear at the best of times, was now slurred with drink. The gist of it seemed to be a party down aft to which the Senior Apprentice was invited. This in itself was unusual for socialising of this type between bridge and fo'c'sle was definitely frowned upon. However Doherty was persuasive and with the earnest cunning of the drunk, was not to be denied. To the drowsy Junior Apprentice it seemed there were women on board and their services were being offered gratis to the Senior Apprentice. This mumbled discourse went on for twenty minutes or so.

The Junior Apprentice was a second tripper and no stranger to the drunken maunderings of seamen; he got bored and fell off to sleep. However it transpired that the fireman's offer to the Senior Apprentice was too insistent to be refused. The Junior Apprentice awoke as the cabin door swung closed and found himself alone in the cabin. Some sixth sense warned him that all might not be well; so he carefully reached down the heavy chromed torch from its hook on the bulkhead and placed it under his pillow before dropping off again.

He was next awakened by incoherent mumblings in his ear and by the feel of rough hands caressing the base of his spine. Despite his preparations he was petrified, nothing in all his sixteen and a half years had given him the remotest idea as to how this attention should be handled. All he could do was to cringe more deeply into the blankets, reach under the pillow for the torch and repeat in a hoarse scared whisper "Don't be a fool, don't be a fool." How long this would have continued, or what the outcome would have been will never be known, for at the critical moment of either surrender or retaliation with the torch, the Senior Apprentice reappeared convinced that he had been turned out for no useful purpose. He was more experienced than the Junior, nineteen years old with three of them spent at sea on a tramp ship, but he had no firm idea of how to react either. His shouted "Get to Hell out of here." was instinctive rather than commanding. It was however imperative enough to scare off Frank Doherty, which was good, but loud enough to wake the Chief Steward in the adjoining cabin which was not, for it meant that the Mate and the Captain had to know as well. Although both were competent to handle ships in the worst of gales, neither were really equipped to resolve this situation, so they passed it on to the police, who were. For them, dealing with Frank Doherty was simple, but what about the Junior Apprentice? At sixteen and a half he clearly could not be an innocent child, especially after nearly a year at sea. They could not really charge him with anything that would stick, so they contented themselves with cautioning him and passing their report back to the Captain. There was little the Captain could do; police reports such as this could not be pigeon-holed, so he in turn had no option but to pass it on to the company back in London. In that distant Board Room it did not make for a pretty story, but did rate instant action.

Thus fate accomplished the final turn of its wheel, in convicting Frank Doherty it had also ensured the ruin of the Junior Apprentice, for at the end of the trip he was handed back his indentures endorsed with the simple but damning phrase 'Unsuitable for Further Training.'

Chapter 39

**Ordinary Seaman Sam Smith
and the Mountie**

It was on the Canadian West Coast. It could have been any one of the thirty odd small ports we visited during our two year charter to MacMillan and Bloedel. Most probably it was either Ocean Falls or Powell River. Certainly it was not Vancouver, for not only does that city have a large waterfront, it also has its own police force, not the Mounties. Be that as it may it was in one of these that Ordinary Seaman Sam Smith learned two more lessons in the art of growing up.

We had been playing football on a snowbound pitch above the town. There was really little else we could do that late on a Saturday afternoon. The one bar was not yet open, the shops were closed and the next cinema show was the Sunday midnight one. The game had been a bit scrappy, but then the pitch was no great shakes either. It had only four notable features; a rather wayward slope towards the left hand downtown corner flag, the sombre pine forest framing three of its sides, a warning notice not to feed wild bears and a slushy trampled path crossing the pitch diagonally from touchline to touchline. This path caused several hold ups during the game as it was the principle pedestrian access from the outlying houses to the vast sawmill that dominated the tiny quayside. To the passing figures hunched into their heavy winter gear it must have been obvious that we were heirs to the race Kipling found going out in the Midday Sun. We played only a brief half hour each way, by which time we were sodden and frozen stiff, and anyway the bar was then open.

Gratefully we sat at the small rickety tables. We would have been happier standing around the pot bellied iron stove, but it was one of the vagaries of the local law that in public rooms you had to be seated to drink. Slowly we began to thaw out and feel human once more. It even became possible to smile and speak with lips no longer stiffened into a frosty semi-mobility. Our fingertips started to ache with the pain of returning circulation; benumbed toes regained enough feeling to remind us that they were still damp and freezingly cold. Life was becoming better with increasing warmth and were we not all shipmates together. Sam was the youngest of our group, and almost the youngest of the whole ship's crew, barely nineteen years old yet already a veteran, quite at home in waterfront bars and bordellos all round the world. However he did not really look his age, his cheeks and chin still carried the razor free fluff of adolescence as well as the scars of an acne not yet fully conquered by maturity.

We had only downed a couple of rounds before half the town's police force marched in, a burly six foot four inches of RCMP Constable, a routine visit to ensure that the strangers in town were no threat to its good order. The other half of the force was presumably tied down with an inevitability of office work. The Constable did not wear the traditional khaki hat and scarlet tunic which are nowadays reserved for formal occasions such as duty outside the Parliament House in Ottawa. The blue trousers with their distinctive double yellow stripe were still there, but not as breeches fitted into bright brown riding boots, but with knife edge creases surmounting a pair of American armed forces style patent leather black shoes. The whole was topped by a plain blue reefer jacket and peaked cap. Even allowing for this more prosaic uniform the Mountie still made an impressive figure as he surveyed the drinkers at the tables.

There was obviously no unseemly behaviour requiring his official attention, none of us had as yet time enough to get drunk and anyway we were far too cold to feel like being disorderly. However something seemed to be worrying the Mountie and he strode over to us, fixing young Sam with a steely gaze. "How old are you?" The 'R U 18' signs in pubs at home flashed across Sam's mind. This was not the first time an over zealous official had questioned his legal right to drink in public. He had nothing to fear. "Nineteen, why?" perhaps a shade too self righteously truculent. "Out, Sonny." Just two words, but their portent was as obvious as the Mountie's official status - and his towering bulk.

As Sam left, discomforted and alone, he learned two more lessons in life. Firstly that not all countries have the same laws and that in Canada at nineteen there was then still another two years of growing up before being allowed to drink with the men. Secondly that if you get slung out of a bar you cannot expect your mates to leave in sympathy with you, especially in the sub-zero temperatures of a Canadian winter.

Chapter 40

**Sammy Logan,
Cook**

"It was like a fight between a fox and a Chief Steward." The small figure, relaxed and off duty, was referring to a hard won bargain with a bumboat man. It's result was the proudly displayed pair of gingery brown shoes lined up by his bunk. To some they might be 'Brothel Creepers' but not to Doc. Their crepe soles, as he knew only too well, would never stop squeaking up and down those dimly lit, bead curtained corridors - but for him such visits were now things of the past - so to Doc 'Brothel Creepers' they were not.

You could tell Sammy Logan was off duty, not only because he was sitting in his cabin, but also from the way he was dressed. In his galley he always wore a grubby white singlet, grubby white cotton trousers, a grubby white apron, on his head an only marginally less soiled chef's beret and on his feet shoes turned into a livid patchwork of cooking fat colours. Now he had changed into a cleaner singlet and trousers, removed the sweat rag and encased his feet in a pair of greasy red felt carpet slippers. These latter were his trade mark. When he was wearing them he was definitely off duty, when he changed back into his workaday shoes he considered himself back in charge of his galley.

Sammy Logan was known as Doc, as was every other Chief Cook on tramp ships, almost no one knew his name was Samuel, certainly no one on board called him Sammy. He was a wizened little man, desiccated was the only way to describe him. It was as though years of bending over a hot stove in a ship's tiny galley had dried every last particle of fat off his slight frame; and looking at his greasy working rig you might be pardoned for thinking you could see where most of it had ended up. It was a constant battle to keep the galley clean, with its continuously burning stoves and its open coal bunker in the corner. Somewhere along the years it had got the better of Doc, and although the galley was cleaned daily his working rig was not: by the end of the week his singlet, trousers and apron could have stood up by

130

themselves. Still he did have his standards. The cigarette that now dangled from his lower lip was always thrown away before he handled food and his pots were scoured after every use. His cooking, though not inspired, was adequate for hungry men living a healthy open air life and as he was fond of saying "I've never poisoned anyone yet, at least, not by accident."

His job, which over the course of years had dried his body to a crisp, had likewise honed his native Cockney humour and he was acknowledged as the ship's wit. In general his forays had himself, the Cook, as their hero, the Chief Steward or the Ship's Chandlers as the villains, in a running battle to palm him off with cheap, bad or inadequate stores. He had only one description of his opponents, they "...were tighter than a crab's arse, and that's watertight." Doc also had a fund of spontaneous humour, generally 'in' jokes with little relevance outside the ship's closed community. Typical of these was the occasion when faced with the meagre portion of bacon allocated for the crew's breakfast his face broke into a seraphic smile and chortled "This ship is certainly a good feeder. There are only fifty of us aboard yet I've more than enough here to feed the whole crew, and all the passengers of a bloody pilgrim ship registered in Mecca as well." It was also standard when handing out the crew's Sunday dinner to quip "Here we are boys, Sunday Sex, Virgin Chicken, all legs and no breast." However there was one subject on which he was very touchy and about which he never made cracks, nor tolerated others to make them. This was the yellowy orange vegetable he was forced to serve at least three times a week under the name by which it was described on all ship's stores returns, turnip. It was in fact the cheaper, humbler swede, and where the difference in cost was accounted no one ever knew. Doc's main grievance appeared to be that he suspected the Chief Steward of receiving backhanders none of which came his way.

Every shipboard job has an element of routine, but with Doc the routine was almost total. At sea and in port the crew demanded three meals a day, seven days a week, and he had to cook every one of them. Stores were purchased in bulk for a standard menu, the week's daily variety being exactly replicated seven days later. The staples of potatoes, root vegetables, frozen meat and flour were replenished as a matter of course; only if other items were unexpectedly cheap would any variation be introduced into the food served at sea. In port there might be fresh green vegetables if they were cheap enough; they might even last for a few days after sailing. Occasionally there might be fresh fruit, but only if there was a glut ashore as bulk purchases of dried apricots, apples and prunes were nearly always cheaper. Fresh meat would be supplied if it was cheaper than frozen carcasses, but fresh milk, never. In all his years at sea Doc had only once seen fresh milk supplied to a British ship. On that one occasion, after six months on the Australian coast, the local Seamen's Union had insisted that even British ships must comply with the Australian seamen's scale of provisions. That once, the ship had flowed with milk, real cow's milk, and in lieu of honey there had been ice cream and fresh lettuce. Their cost must have broken the Chief Steward's heart, but by careful pruning of the homeward stores he managed to avoid the worst of the owner's wrath. On that homeward trip the 'pound and pint' of the Merchant Shipping Act was so stringently observed that even Doc's caustic wit was stilled.

So for all his working life it had been the unadventurous same for Sammy Logan; chicken on Sunday, pea soup on Tuesday, kedgeree on Thursday, and all the other dishes in their constant seven day rotation come winter, summer, storm or flat calm. However cooking in a winter gale could be an adventure in itself. As the ship climbed each wave the pots would slide to one side of the stove only to be saved from falling off by the fiddles[1] at its edge. Then with a crash which sent showers of steaming water across the galley they would go back at a run as the ship slid down into the trough. At these times Doc and his two assistants needed all their agility to avoid serious scalding, and all their strength to keep the meals on the stove and off the deck. Culinary skill came a poor second, and perseverence under the most trying conditions became the paramount requirement. But no matter how harassed he might be Doc was always ready with a sardonic crack, such as "It's a good job she's rolling like a bastard; you'll need some help to digest this rubbish." This, at the height of a force nine Atlantic gale with the decks awash, the Galley Boy seasick below and the Second Cook out of action with a scalded arm, showed the true mettle of the little Cockney.

The Cook prided himself on being the complete cynic, viewing the human race with detached amusement, but he had one very human failing of his own, bumboats. They were his great weakness as witnessed by his new crepe soled shoes; they really were hideous ginger and had cost at least half as much again as in a shoe shop at home. But at a full pound off the bumboatman's original asking price Doc was content with his bargain. There was something in the way these itinerant traders spread their wares on the deck that he found irresistible. They always came aboard in bunkering ports, rarely in loading or discharging ports as the decks were then too cluttered with cargo gear. In the coaling ports they made a colourful break in an otherwise dreary existence, and while most of the crew were content to look on, Doc bargained and bought. It was selective buying though, he picked only the acknowledged best; butterfly wing trays in Rio, hand tailored suits in Hong Kong, carved hardwood elephants in Colombo, tea sets in Japan. His buys were either clothing or souvenirs. The clothing was readily usable but Doc, a bachelor with no close family ties, found the souvenirs a problem. His cabin was always festooned with his latest acquisitions plus one or two favourites from previous voyages. Whenever he changed ships, say every two or three trips, Doc found there were more than he could carry down the gangway and inevitably he left some behind every time.

1. Fiddles - *Metal bars fitted on the galley stove to stop pots sliding off when the ship rolled*

Then his cabin seemed more emptied than others. There were a few discarded odds and ends; a plaque of a Spanish dancer askew on the bulkhead and a very small black wooden elephant with only one tusk fallen over on its side on top of the chest of drawers. There too in the corner was a pair of very worn red carpet slippers forlornly awaiting an owner who would never even miss them. Doc was gone. Undoubtedly he would return ere long, not to this ship but some other, to start rebuilding his collection over again. Then too there would be another pair of felt slippers, maybe not red this time, but whatever their colour, his trademark still.

Chapter 41

**Bob Harris,
Donkeyman**

"For we're noo awa to bide awa, we're no awa to leave ye." The traditional words would have been excruciating to the ear of a Scot, but their rendering in thick Scouse drifted quite naturally from the saloon bar of the Iron Duke near the Four Bridges at Birkenhead docks. Inside the pub the evening was drawing to a close and the lead singer was a trifle unsteady on his feet. He was a tall well built man, handsome in a rather heavy way, with dark hair curling over a broad low forehead. Dressed in an electric blue drape gaberdine suit and a hand painted silk tie he could only have been a seaman for such clothes were not found in a Britain just emerging from the utility era. After a few more pints and a spirited rendering of 'Maggie May' the singer sat down more than half drunk; sweat ran down his face, his tie was loosened, his top shirt button undone.

"Just as well I'm here," thought the pert blonde sitting beside him, "for he'd not make it alone." but there pride rather than bitterness in her tone, for this was her man. It was she who would put him to bed and then snuggle up to his warm body. This would be more than sufficient reward, for though they were married it was indeed seldom that he was home to share her lonely nights. This was her accepted way of life. In neighbouring back to back terraced houses there were many other families where the man was at sea, and she doubted if she would ever have it otherwise. Besides her man although not yet thirty was at the top of his profession and this gave her a very definite standing in the street. Her Bob was the Donkeyman of the Atlantic Wanderer. His job the engine room counterpart of the Bosun. It was a responsible job and although he was much younger than most he had still fought his way up the conventional route through the rates of Fireman Trimmer and Greaser. His determination to get to the top had enabled him to move up faster than most. Bob had been a Donkeyman for two years and married for almost half that time, both successes that gave him a warm glow whenever he thought of them.

134

Later he stirred in his sleep and the smaller body curled inside his sighed contentedly as it nuzzled into a more comfortable position. This was sufficient to wake him. "Hey there, la, do you come here often?" he murmured. "Only in the mating season, Wack." she answered sleepily, as she drew him into her yet again.

Still later; "Hey there, la, this time tomorrow we'll be away." "You what? What y're doing focking talking then, Wack, let's have some action." she responded, happy now, but not without pangs for the days to come.

It was a night Bob Harris was to recall many times in the ensuing months from Liverpool to Spain for rock salt; from Japan to Vancouver for timber; then from Australia back to the UK in grain. At ten knots that meant home was still many more lonely nights away.

Chapter 42

Exodus

Four years on, John, now with a brand new Second Mate's Ticket, reviewed his career to date, and his ambitions. The sea was still beckoning, but sex had also reared its head. John rather fancied himself in whites (tramp ship officers wore khaki drill in the tropics); walking the deck when off watch with a passenger - female, young and good looking - on his arm (tramp ships had no promenade decks and were an all male environment anyway). So putting on his best suit John visited the London Office of one of the biggest liner companies. They were obviously impressed, or so John thought, and were about to offer him a berth, then his time at the Mercury as recorded on his CV was noticed. "I'm sorry, but I'm afraid you went to the wrong school." An instant rebuff, but John was nothing if not resourceful. Schooling he could now do nothing about, but improved social status maybe he could. So John once more donned his suit and visited the Admiralty.

They too were interested. A qualified Merchant Officer of John's obvious ability was what they really needed in the Royal Naval Reserve, which latter represented the cream of the mercantile marine. John's head swelled and he shook hands, turning to go, but just before the door closed. "Wait a moment. You're not quite the run of the mill Third Mate, are you?" There were John knew some unusual entries for a tramp ship officer on his CV, perhaps his time as a Cathedral Chorister, perhaps his general Schools Matric obtained by a correspondence course with the College of the Sea.

Perhaps he should have sensed a trap for the unwary, but instead his head swelled two more sizes. "Why not join as a career Royal Navy officer?" The late lamented declined Dartmouth scholarship flashed before John's eyes. Now they were talking. Papers and brochures were laid out on the desk before him, and once again agreement reached before he turned to go, but again before he got to the door. "With your special attributes why not fly with the Navy?" The hook had been well baited. If his head had not been so swollen John might have questioned the relevance of any of his skills to flying, but he did not. The die was cast, and he was at least three month's into aircrew training before he realised that the shortage of possible candidates made flying training the number one priority for all current naval recruiting. And so John's short career in the Merchant Navy ended.

The author notes that this is truly autobiographical. Moreover this chapter was written some time before he first heard the apocryphal story of the officer who said "I was not good enough to join the P & O so I joined the Royal Navy!"

Postscript

I am privileged to write this postscript from the view of an owner that runs a modern fleet of cargo vessels into the twenty-first century. Our ships spend as little time in port as possible; it is the only way for us to compete, be profitable and invest for the future.

Life on board for today's seafarers is very different to the picture painted by these pages. The inexorable march of technology has had a dramatic effect on the mariner's role. Seafaring, of course, has always been reliant on certain basic skills, but today many of even the seemingly fundamental ingredients of the task have changed out of all recognition.

Spare time is at a premium as the modern seafarer will be expected to work a huge proportion of his on board hours. Time off duty is needed for rest; now leave is just about the only opportunity for social and other pursuits. This is, of course, the way of the developed economies, but crews of third world traders into newly developing countries may well still experience some of the way of life described in this book.

I am grateful to Tom Peppitt for setting down these fascinating chapters reflecting the ways of the British Merchant Marine half a century ago. It provides an important historical perspective and comparison with life at sea in the new millennium. In no way should it be seen as an advertisement for recruitment; life at sea is not like that today!

Michael Everard CBE BA
F T Everard & Sons Limited
London

Photo Sources

The photographs included are intended to reflect the period and environment of the narrative. Many of the people, ships and other subjects illustrated are not those referred to in the text.

Chapters 1, 18, - National Maritime Museum, London
Chapters 2, 9, 15, 16, 19, 22, 31, 37 - Museum of London, PLA Collection
Chapter 3 - Hamble-le-Rice Parish Council
Chapters 4, 10, 13, 20, 25, 29, 36 - Trustees of the Imperial War Museum, London
Chapters 5, 39 - David Milne
Chapters 6, 11 - Stan Mayes
Chapters 7, 12, 24, 33, 35, 42 - Ruth Holmes, ex Peter Holmes collection
Chapter 8 - Lt Cdr (SCC) Geoff Preshner MBE RNR
Chapters 14, 23, 32 - The Mission to Seafarers
Chapter 17 - Paul Joannou, Official Historian, Newcastle United
Chapters 21, 38, 40 - Topham Picturepoint
Chapter 26 - Maritime Photo Library
Chapter 27 - Shaftesbury Homes & Arethusa
Chapter 28 - The Peninsular and Oriental Steam Navigation Company
Chapter 30 - Ray Sturtivant ISO
Chapter 34 - Ron Phillips
Chapter 41 - Birkenhead Central Library

Publisher's Thanks

The gathering of photographs to illustrate these chapters was no easy task. Whilst profiles and other views of ships of the period proliferate, arguably the crews were as much ignored by the camera as by many of the shipowners themselves. Ultimately, with the assistance of museums, maritime charities, photo libraries, shipping companies and many retired seafarers and their families it has been possible to add pictures to the words. A big thank you to all who helped, not just those sources which appear in the list above, but also to those who sent photographs which in the event were not included.

My thanks also go to the author, Tom Peppitt, who has been quick to deal with queries and corrections as the pre-production stages have evolved. Last but not least, thanks to David Milne who proof read and played Devil's Advocate over a number of issues, the book much the better for his input.

Richard Walsh, Chaffcutter Books